TRIBE *of* MILLIONAIRES

WHAT IF ONE CHOICE COULD CHANGE EVERYTHING?

NEW YORK TIMES BESTSELLING AUTHORS
DAVID OSBORN & PAT HIBAN
with **MIKE McCARTHY & TIM RHODE**

FOREWORD BY HAL ELROD

A GoBundance Publication

Cover design by Dino Marino
Interior design by Dino Marino

ISBN: 978-0-9982882-2-2
eISBN: 978-0-9982882-3-9

OTHER BOOKS BY THE AUTHORS OF
TRIBE OF MILLIONAIRES

David Osborn (with Paul Morris)

Wealth Can't Wait : Avoid the 7 Wealth Traps , Implement the 7 Business Pillars , and Complete a Life Audit Today!!!

David Osborn (with Hal Elrod)

Miracle Morning Millionaires : What the wealthy do before 8.00 a.m. that will make you rich

Pat Hiban

6 Steps to 7 Figures : A Real Estate Professional's Guide to Building Wealth and Creating Your Own Destiny

Mike McCarthy (with Hal Elrod, Lindsay McCarthy and Honorée Corder)

The Miracle Morning for Parents and Families : How to Bring out the best in your KIDS and your SELF

Tim Rhode

1 Life Roadmap Journal : The Basic Inner Coding Needed to Dream, Plan and LIVE your best Life.

PRAISE FOR
TRIBE OF MILLIONAIRES

*"A wonderful story and a compelling guide to why
surrounding yourself with the right people
is so important to success."*

Jeff Hoffman, serial entrepreneur
and co-founder of Priceline.com

*"This book has the potential to open your eyes
to the hidden forces that are determining your life."*

Rob Dial, founder of MWF Motivation Podcast

*"My eyebrows nearly jumped off my face with excitement
when I started reading* Tribe of Millionaires.
*Why? Because I love business books that teach lessons
through a realistic parable. This book kept me fully engaged
from the first page to the last. You're going absolutely to love it!"*

Dr. Sean Stephenson, author of *Get Off Your 'But' -
How to End Self-Sabotage and Stand Up for Yourself*

HOW STRONG IS *YOUR* TRIBE?

This book includes FREE access to the
GoBundance **Tribal Strength Assessment.**

Get your personalized results and learn how
to strengthen your tribe and transform your life at:

www.TribeOfMillionaires.com

TABLE OF CONTENTS

FOREWORD BY HAL ELROD i

INTRODUCTION - THE STORY BEFORE THE STORY iii

CHAPTER 1 - THE HAIL MARY 1

CHAPTER 2 - THE TICKET 7

CHAPTER 3 - THE FIRST EFFECT 15

CHAPTER 4 - THE TRIBE 25

CHAPTER 5 - THE SECOND EFFECT..................................33

CHAPTER 6 - THE THIRD EFFECT...................................49

CHAPTER 7 - ONE SHEET TO RULE THEM ALL.........................61

CHAPTER 8 - THE FOURTH EFFECT 73

CHAPTER 9 - THE GROTTO 87

CHAPTER 10 - THE FIFTH EFFECT 97

CHAPTER 11 - THE CLIMB 109

CHAPTER 12 - THE SIXTH EFFECT.................................. 119

CHAPTER 13 - THE GIFT..131

CHAPTER 14 - HOME... 141

LESSONS - TRIBE OF MILLIONAIRES 149

GOBUNDANCE - THE "REAL" TRIBE OF MILLIONAIRES.................151

PROFILE - DIEGO CORZO 153

PROFILE - AARON AMUCHASTEGUI 155

PROFILE - JOHN EDWIN......................................157

PROFILE - DANIEL DEL REAL...............................159

PROFILE - WALLY ELIBIARY 161

PROFILE - JOHN WHITE......................................163

ARE YOU READY TO PLAY AT A HIGHER LEVEL?.........165

ABOUT THE AUTHORS..167

ACKNOWLEDGEMENTS 171

FOREWORD
BY HAL ELROD

There's a certain irony in me being the first person you hear from on this journey.

I'm probably best known for writing a book called *The Miracle Morning*, that teaches you to wake up before everyone else and spend time in solitude. It's a practice that helps you take control of the most important part of the day so that you can transform your life.

But there's more to life than mornings. There's a whole busy day that follows—a day of decisions to make, businesses to run, and work to do. Unlike the morning, navigating the rest of the day successfully is anything but solitary. Creating the life you want, it turns out, is very much a team sport.

The famous author and entrepreneur Jim Rohn knew this well. His claim that you become the average of the five people you spend the most time with is perhaps the most important piece of wisdom I know. I believe those words hold the secret to finding everything you want in life.

Yet, as profound and essential as they are, they're almost universally ignored—when it comes to Jim's words, we tend to be all talk, no walk.

The authors of this book are on a mission to change that. GoBundance is a group for men and women who want to lead epic lives— lives filled with health, wealth, generosity and strong, connected relationships.

When I attended my first GoBundance event, I was still working on my business dream of reaching $1 million in annual revenue. I quickly doubled that after joining, and I've never looked back.

But GoBundance is much more than entrepreneurship and so much more than networking. At its core, the group revolves around a deep commitment to the things that are most important in life— things like relationships, health, and abundance.

That was a commitment I needed to learn.

I used to say that family was the most important thing in the world. And I *believed* what I was saying, too. Then I got cancer.

That experience quickly woke me up to the fact that I was talking the relationship talk, but I was far from walking it. I was doing exactly what I'd seen so many others do: ignore just how important the people around you truly are, and how profound their impact is.

Too many entrepreneurs say that family is their number one priority. Yet their lives tell a very different story. They are overscheduled, overworked, and often overwhelmed.

With the help of GoBundance, I've gone from saying and believing that relationships are the most important thing in my world to actually aligning my life with that philosophy. Because of it, my business *and* my life have flourished.

If you've struggled to make change, or it seems like you've done everything right and something still seems wrong, my bet is that you're disconnected from the fundamental truth that *who you surround yourself with determines your future.*

Your opportunity to rediscover that truth—and change your life—lies in this remarkable story.

Yours in abundance,
Hal Elrod
GoBundance Member & Author of *The Miracle Morning*

INTRODUCTION
THE STORY BEFORE THE STORY

Once upon a time…

Two guys meet at a real estate industry event. True story. We'll call them David and Pat, because those are their real names.

At the time, they were both hard-charging entrepreneurs in their 30s. A little competitive by nature, a little driven by design, these two go-getters had an idea: *What if they could be better together than apart?*

We know what you're thinking—that they joined their companies and created an epic new business that took over the world.

Wrong.

In fact, they kept their own businesses, but they used the power of working together to become more accountable, to leverage each other's talents, and to support each other when the going got tough.

It was a knock-out success.

One went on to become the top ReMax real estate agent in the *world.* The other built a nine-figure net worth (and counting) and became a *New York Times* bestselling author. (And lest you think it was all work, no play, they also traveled the world with their families, transformed their health, and gave a whole lot back, too.)

Along the way, their little accountability experiment grew. One day at an industry event in Chicago, Pat met Tim, who would transform the group's values to embrace contribution and a more balanced life. Later, Mike and Rock would also join, helping to lead the tribe's beginning as a mastermind.

They got better at working together and supporting each other. They built a specialized toolkit of processes and techniques to help leverage the power of groups. And somewhere, on a long road trip across the southern US, they came up with a new idea: *What if we took what we have and brought it to EVERYONE?*

Right then, on that hot, straight line across Texas, GoBundance was born.

GoBundance is a unique, group-based approach to help entrepreneurs and business professionals lead epic lives. It's a way of using the power of like-minded people to do more than you ever could alone—not just in business, but in your health, your relationships, and your lasting legacy here on the planet.

That little idea—that we're better together than apart—is what started all of this, and it's what this book is about. What you're reading is our best effort to convince you that no matter what you think you can do alone (or better yet, what you think you *can't*), you can do it faster, better, easier, and—best of all—*more happily*, with others.

What follows is a story about the power of groups to transform your life. It's about how something magical happens when you put the right people together in the right ways. It's about how groups can not only help entrepreneurs grow their businesses, but how they can help them heal, forge enduring friendships, and, when all is said and done, find peace in a world where peace isn't always easy.

Abundantly yours,

The Founders of GoBundance

P.S. This book is a fictional story, but like any good tale, it has its roots in truth. To discover the real-life transformational stories of GoBundance members, read on to the end…

CHAPTER 1
THE HAIL MARY

I sat in the car and listened to the rain hammer the roof.

Hail Mary Friday, I thought. *How appropriate.*

I looked at the building through the beating windshield wipers. It was a sprawling century home at the edge of town—one of those majestic places with just the right amount of haunted-house curb appeal.

At least I'm dressed for the occasion, I thought.

That was the only positive thing that I could come up with: I was appropriately dressed. Sad, but true.

The steady drum of the rain let up. I took a deep breath and stepped out into the drizzle.

* * *

It was Jasmine who started calling it "Hail Mary" Friday. Leave it to my wife to nail the perfect combination of brutal honesty and optimism.

It was also Jas who pulled the suit out of the deep recesses of my closet. After some complaining on my part, I agreed to wear it.

She straightened my tie. "You look handsome," she said.

"I think I look desperate."

"Honey," she said, patting my chest. "You are."

"Very funny. I feel like a beggar. Like I'm asking for handouts."

"How about we call it asking for help, instead? People actually do that, you know."

"Not this guy."

She was right, though. This was a last-chance situation and I needed help. Or a miracle, perhaps. My startup company had burned through cash like it was on fire. Everything had taken longer than expected. Two years had seemed to vanish, and now I was facing my worst nightmare: we were completely out of money.

Every direction I looked was as gloomy as the rain I was now walking through. It wasn't just the looming failure of the business. That was bad enough. But if I didn't find a fresh infusion of cash, I wasn't going to make payroll. I had a team of a dozen people counting on me. Their families, in turn, counted on them. I felt buried alone under a mountain of responsibility—a mountain that was about to let loose an avalanche of disappointment.

In a last-ditch attempt to hold back the crash, I'd arranged two meetings for today—what had become Hail Mary Friday. More than two meetings would have been better, but I'd already called in every favor and connection I had to fund the business in the first place. My options were limited.

Somehow, I hated that part the most—the asking for help. For favors. In the end, though, I'd ended up with two meetings. Two chances to save my business.

I'd blown them both.

In both meetings—one over coffee, one over a desk—I knew the answer was *no* before I'd finished shaking hands. The rest of the time was just awkwardly running out the clock, everyone knowing the outcome, everyone waiting to move on.

I could hardly blame them, really. My company was in serious trouble, and I didn't have anything reassuring to say. *I just need more time* wasn't an investor pitch. It was the flailing, hail-Mary pass of a losing quarterback.

Two chances. Two failures.

And now this.

So much for Hail Mary Friday.

* * *

As I tugged opened the front door of the old brick mansion, I felt a twinge of resentment. *Why now?* This was like kicking a man while he was down. It felt so unfair.

Just get it over with, I thought. I'd show my face, and then I'd head home to forget this week and avoid thinking about the one to come.

A deep voice pulled me from my self-pity. Just inside the door, a tall, bald man in a black suit stood as if waiting for me.

"Good afternoon," he repeated. "Can I help you?"

The man was in his fifties, I guessed, but he was a fit fifty. Tanned and lean, he stood tall, with a kind face.

I looked past him into a wide atrium lined with a series of dark wooden doors. Each bore a small sign.

I looked back to the man. "Martinez," I said.

The bald man paused, then nodded ever so slightly.

"It'll be the quiet one," I added.

He said nothing, but I thought I detected something around his eyes. Something that said, *Really? Are you so sure?*

All he said was, "The second door on the left."

I walked down the hall, but before I'd even reached the door, I knew it was the wrong one. I could hear the dull roar of a crowd from inside, and I looked back down the entryway, counting doors, looking for the one I must have missed.

The bald man at the entrance caught my confused look and nodded at me, adding, "That's the Martinez gathering."

I shrugged, turned the handle, then pushed the door open.

* * *

The room was packed. And not just with quiet groups of subdued funeral goers. It was *alive*. The noise I'd heard outside the door was a pale shadow of what was going on inside.

There were groups of people everywhere, nestled together, holding drinks, laughing. Young kids ran around the room. Teenagers stood, awkward, but not unhappy, against the far wall. Everywhere in the room I looked there were people. Everywhere I looked there was *life*.

Except one place.

There, in an open casket at the front of the room, lay my father.

I slipped quietly through the crowd.

To one side of his coffin stood five men. All of different ages, but all dressed in identical black suits. The same suits, I realized, that the bald man at the front door had worn. The same healthy—and now that I saw them together—wealthy look. They just looked... *prosperous*.

At first, I thought they worked for the funeral home. But as I watched, it was clear they were here as guests, not staff. They spoke amongst themselves—nodding, sharing a smile, a pat on the back. It was obvious they knew each other well, and were close.

Who were these men? How did they know my father?

I walked closer to the coffin.

My first thought came out of left field: *He looks better than he did twenty years ago.* That was a surprise. After all—who looks better in a casket than they do alive? Somehow, the years had been kind to my father.

What was more surprising, I hated to admit, was that I'd been keeping track of those years. I was a teenager the last time I'd seen my father. My memories were not fond. He was self-absorbed. A failed businessman, despite being a workaholic. He was also a drunk, and as far as I knew, friendless.

That, I realized, was the biggest surprise of all. I was here for the funeral of a man who I assumed had died broke, unhappy, and alone.

Instead, I found a room filled with vibrant energy. Filled with a *community*. It made no sense. Unless funeral homes were hiring extras, something had changed in my father's life.

As I stood there, the room grew quiet.

One of the five men approached the coffin. He patted my father's hand affectionately, almost as if he were still alive. Then he placed a small white card under the clasped hands, paused a moment, then stepped away. His eyes shone with tears.

Behind him, another man in a black suit did the same. Then another. Each man's interaction was slightly different. But they all did the same two things: placed a small white card under my father's hands, and stepped away in tears to join the rest of the suited men. Finally, the bald man stepped up to the casket, and tucked a final card in with the rest.

I looked down at the collection of six cards. Each one was embossed with a simple monogram:

T o M

I looked closer. There seemed to be words written on each card, but the text was too small to read.

My curiosity flared up. *What was on the cards? Who were these men?* For the first time in two decades, I realized I actually wanted to know something about my father's life.

Before I could look closer, however, the six men moved to flank the coffin, three on each side.

Too little too late, I thought, and felt an unexpected pang of regret.

The bald man—the one from the front door—closed the lid of the coffin gently.

Then, as if moving as one, the six men lifted the coffin from its pedestal, and carried my father from the funeral home and out of my life for good.

* * *

The rain had let up by the time I left, but I felt unsettled inside. For years, I'd told myself a story about an isolated, selfish man. A man who didn't know his priorities. A man who had no time for his family.

I couldn't reconcile that with what I'd seen inside. A room filled with people who, at least as far as I could see, genuinely cared about the man lying in the casket.

A sadness spread through my chest. *Had I gotten it all wrong? What had happened over those twenty years?*

I walked down the wet sidewalk to the curb and noticed the same tall bald man from inside walking down the street. A long black car pulled alongside, and he gracefully stepped in, the car barely slowing. In a hiss of wet tires, the limo was gone.

Nice ride, I thought. Apparently, my father had traded up in the friends department.

When I reached the curb, I could see paper under the windshield wiper of my car.

Great, I thought. *Your business is failing. Your father is dead. For the perfect Hail Mary Friday trifecta, here's a parking ticket.*

It wasn't a ticket. Tucked under the wiper was a small envelope with *Ethan* written neatly on the front.

Inside was a simple card, just like the ones in my father's casket. On one side were the same embossed letters:

T o M

I flipped it over. In the same neat handwriting as the envelope was the following:

Ethan,

We need to discuss your father's estate.

S.

CHAPTER 2
THE TICKET

In the end, of course, it was Jas who convinced me to go.

"He's just trying to control me," I said. "This is just like when I was a kid. It's the same thing all over again."

"Ethan," she said gently. "Your father is dead."

When she said it that way, it made me feel a little foolish. *He is dead,* I thought. *What harm can there be in finding out who he was?*

That was immediately followed by a sense of sadness. *My father is dead.*

I pushed it away.

Jas was right. But what really tipped the scales was the argument that neither one of us wanted to speak aloud. It was like a checklist that I knew we were both ticking off on our mental fingers:

1. We were broke.
2. We were just about to get a lot more broke. We were going to lose the business, and almost certainly our home.
3. A mysterious stranger named "S." had just invited me to discuss my father's estate. (Really? Who signs things with just an initial, anyway?)
4. This "S" had a hell of a nice suit, and left in hell of a long limo.

It was a compelling list, but it made me feel squeamish. Like I was a cliched TV villain, rubbing my hands in glee as a casket was lowered into the ground.

Still, it was hard to ignore what might have just landed in my lap. The business was in serious trouble, and maybe this was the miracle we needed. Was it possible that Hail Mary Friday hadn't been a failure after all?

"Does walking away from this do anything good?" Jas asked.

I had no answer to that. Which, I figured, was the same as saying, "No."

* * *

That was how, after a night of painful soul-searching, I found myself at the address written on the back of the crisp, white card that the mysterious "S" had left on my car.

I looked out and up through the windshield, craning my neck to see the sleek glass skyscraper that towered over the block. I'd never been in the building, but I knew the address. It was in one of the most expensive commercial districts in the city.

Thank God it's Saturday, I thought. I wasn't sure I had a credit card with enough space for parking.

I stepped through the front door to find a vast, marble-floored atrium. At the opposite side, I could see a reception desk. I walked toward it, my footsteps echoing across the high glass ceilings, trying to look as if a guy who couldn't afford parking actually belonged here.

Finally, I gave up trying to be cool and simply gazed around in wonder. *This place is huge.* Had my father worked here? I had no idea. I knew nothing about him, beyond my unpleasant childhood memories.

Still, I couldn't help but speculate. The closer I'd gotten to downtown that morning, the more I'd begun to wonder. I had absolutely no idea what his estate was worth, if anything. But still... was this my Hail Mary? My miracle?

Don't be weak, said a voice in my head. *You don't need charity.*

But I needed *something*. My father had never given me anything as a kid. I had to find my own way, make my own money, build my own life. Maybe now was my chance to get something from him, even if it was just money.

"Sir?"

I jerked back to reality. A receptionist-slash-security guard stood at the desk, his hands clasped behind his back.

"I..." I trailed off. I didn't know what to say. Was there a law office here? I had no suite number, not even a floor. I didn't even know the *name* of the person I was supposed to meet. What was I supposed to do? Wink and say, "*S* sent for me, my good man," and then wait for the secret door to open? This wasn't James Bond. People didn't go by letters in real life.

"Sir?"

With no idea what else to do, I finally reached into my pocket and handed him the white card with the embossed letters. *T o M.*

"Yes sir," the man said. He reached below the desk, and I heard the *click* of a button.

The wall beside the desk slid open to reveal an elevator.

I'll be damned.

"Let me guess. There's a martini in there? Shaken, not stirred?"

"Sir?"

"Never mind."

But I thought I saw just a hint of a smile.

* * *

The elevator opened on an enormous office. Not into a hallway, or waiting room, but *right into* the office. After a brief pause, I stepped into a breathtaking, modern room. The walls were almost entirely glass, punctuated by the odd stretch of bare concrete graced with stunning artwork.

There was a sitting area of leather couches. Across from that, a large conference table. Illuminated glass art cases rose from the floor on concrete pedestals.

"Hello Ethan," said a deep voice.

I turned to see the tall bald man, once again in his black suit. *The mysterious S*, I thought.

He stepped from behind an old desk—it seemed tiny compared to the rest of the room--and strode to greet me.

"Thank you so much for making the time for me," he said. "My name is Simon. I was one of your father's closest friends."

I felt an unexpected pang of jealousy.

Simon seemed to sense my discomfort. "I know you and your father weren't close. My job is… well, first things first. Please," he said, "make yourself comfortable."

Simon had a formal, almost old-fashioned, manner. He spoke clearly, and for the first time I picked up a hint of an accent. South African? Something European? It made him all the more mysterious.

He motioned to one of the two chairs facing the tiny worn desk. As I sat, I could see the same initial carved into the wood of the front. T o M.

As if by magic, a man appeared, carrying a tray of coffee. He offered to pour. I helped myself.

The bald man walked to the window. It was only then that I realized how *high* we were. *This must be the most valuable piece of square footage in the whole city*, I thought. Despite myself, I began to speculate again about my father's will.

"It was your father's wish that I be the executor of his estate," Simon said.

"Is this my father's business?" I asked.

"No. This is the main office of my business. Although your father

THE TICKET • 11

and I worked together many times."

"*Tom*? That's your business? I haven't heard of it."

Simon either hadn't heard, or he was ignoring me. He continued to stare out at the skyline.

"Your father's will is quite specific," he said.

"I can only imagine," I said. It came out a little bitterly.

Simon's eyes never moved from the skyline outside.

"It was his wish that his entire estate pass to you, his sole heir."

I felt my heart quicken a little. *Maybe something good could come of all this*, I thought. It was possible, wasn't it? After all the resentment, the empty years, that perhaps now I was going to see some benefit?

He turned back to me. "There are, however, certain conditions."

And there it was.

Of *course* there were conditions. Weren't there always with my father? Everything was an exchange. Everything was a transaction. This for that, tit for tat.

Simon picked up on my shift in mood and turned back.

"Let me just itemize them for you."

"Sure. Why don't you do that?" *Here we go.*

He sat at the desk and opened a leather-bound folder. He lifted a sheet of paper.

"There is some legalese," he said. "I have a copy here for you. With your permission, I'll read just the salient points."

"Read away." I made no attempt to hide my irritation.

"I, Roberto Martinez, being of sound mind and body, do hereby bequeath my entire estate and all its assets to my only son, Ethan, subject to the following conditions."

I felt my hackles rise at that word again: *conditions.*

"Number one," Simon continued. "Ethan will, within 24 hours, report to the executor of my estate. Number two, Ethan will for seven days remain in the custody of Simon and the other group members.

On day seven, all my assets will be transferred in full to Ethan."

Simon put the paper down. "That is the essence. I should add that any and all expense incurred during the seven days will be covered by the estate. Which includes—"

He lifted some more papers, then pushed a letter-sized envelope toward me. The same T o M logo.

"What's that?" I didn't bother picking it up.

"It's a ticket," Simon said.

"To where?"

Simon didn't answer. He just folded his hands on his desk and waited.

So I waited.

Then waited some more.

"Fine," I said at last. "What do I get?"

"Pardon me?"

I was heating up, now. "What do I get? If this is all just a big trans-action—Ethan does this, and then gets this—then I want to know what I'm getting."

Simon looked at me carefully. "Your father has left you something of great value," he said at last, in his clipped English.

"And that is…?"

"Ethan, your father's legacy is of—well, a specific nature. But I'm afraid I'm forbidden from revealing it until the end of our week together."

That was it. I'd had it. "Oh, I know what the estate is," I said.

Simon cocked his head.

"It's *bullshit*," I said. "Just like everything else about my father." I stood up. "If I learned anything from my father, it was how to cut and run. Thanks for your time, but the answer is no."

I walked to the elevator and stepped inside. I reached over to hit the "1" button. I stopped, my finger poised over the button.

"By the way," I said. "Nice office. Who's Tom?"

"Tom?"

"Your company. I've seen the Tom logo everywhere. You're Simon. Who's Tom?"

"Ah. That I *can* tell you. It's not a name. And it's not my company." The doors began to slide shut.

"It stands for Tribe of Millionaires."

I jammed my hand between the closing doors.

"Tribe of Millionaires?"

Simon just sat still, watching me, his hands still folded on his desk.

I held the elevator doors open.

I had no idea what my father's estate was worth. Perhaps nothing. For all I knew, this really *was* an effort to somehow control me from the grave.

But I also knew a Hail Mary when I saw one. Tribe of Millionaires? Given what I was facing, that sounded like Tribe of *hell yeah* to me.

Which was why, after almost twenty years of intentionally separating myself from a man I barely knew, I found myself doing exactly what he asked.

* * *

I had barely reached the lobby and slid out through the "secret" elevator door when reality set in.

What had I done? It was like my mind had been taken over by someone else. Just seconds after turning down the offer, I'd walked right back into the office and signed the paperwork on Simon's desk. We'd shaken hands, and I'd left holding nothing but a sealed envelope.

Now, here I was standing on the street realizing that I'd just turned the next week of my life over to a perfect stranger.

I felt sick to my stomach. What had I done? My company was running on fumes. I needed to be there 24 hours a day for the next week, not running around with some "tribe" like a trust-fund brat.

Trust-fund brat. Was that what this was? As soon as Simon had said the word 'millionaire,' I'd changed my tune almost instantly. Was that what I was hoping to become?

I knew it wasn't true. What I saw wasn't easy money—it was an opportunity to find financing for the business. If I could get a last-minute investor on board, I was sure we could push through and get to market. I didn't want to be a trust-fund brat. I wanted to create something.

In the meantime, I had work to do. I was leaving in the morning. There were calls to make. I had to pack.

Pack. I looked down at the envelope in my hands. Where was I even going?

I ripped open the envelope, expecting to find a plane ticket. Instead, all I found was another white card, and another address.

CHAPTER 3
THE FIRST EFFECT

Breaking the news that I was leaving turned into a farce worthy of a reality show.

With the exception of Jas, everyone I told—from my assistant to my investors and other team members—thought I'd lost my mind.

"I'm trying to save the company," I told my operations manager, Andrew.

"Great. Where are you going?"

"I have no idea."

"Ooookaaay. Who are you meeting with?"

"I'm not sure."

After a few conversations like that, I gave up trying to explain. I just switched to the "my father passed away," story. Everyone understood that. Everyone except me, that is.

Jasmine sat on the bed while I packed. It seemed to take forever. I had no idea where I was going or what I was doing. Twice I slammed my suitcase shut in frustration, saying, "That's it. I'm not going."

Twice Jasmine calmed me down. "Embrace it, Ethan," she said. "Maybe something good will come from your father after all."

Right. Fat chance of that.

But I thought of Simon's extravagant office, my father's estate. And my own humble office and the people counting on me.

And I kept packing.

* * *

The address on the card was for a private airfield about an hour from the city.

I arrived to find a single plane on the runway—a private jet, shining in the morning sun near a small terminal building.

Simon was waiting on the tarmac. He stood, now casually dressed, the wind ruffling his legs of his pants.

"Where are we going?" I asked.

"Onward," he smiled.

Suitcase in hand, I took a deep breath, looked around the airfield, and climbed the steps.

I ducked my head, stepped inside, then stood and gazed around the luxurious space.

"Is this your first time on a small jet?" Simon asked.

"Is it that obvious?"

Simon smiled again and motioned for me to sit in one of the large leather seats. "Make yourself comfortable," he said, in his clipped English. "We'll be taking off shortly." He took a seat opposite that faced me.

"Look, I appreciate the sense of mystery," I said, "But where are we going? I had a tough time explaining this to the people around me."

Simon cocked his head. "The people around you," he mused. "How perfect."

He reached into the bag at his feet and pulled out the same monogrammed leather folder I'd seen on his desk in the office.

"I'm not trying to be particularly secretive, Ethan," he said as he opened the folder. "I just know from experience—as did your father— that learning new things is a *process*. It happens in small stages. In layers that build over time."

Learning? What was he talking about?

Simon pulled a single piece of paper from the folder. "We have a few hours ahead of us, and I'd like to put them to proper use."

Simon handed me the sheet of paper. It was blank, save for two parallel columns running from top to bottom.

"You mentioned 'the people around you'," he continued. "And that's really the perfect place to begin. While I arrange some details with our pilot, I'd like to offer you a short exercise."

He handed me a pen.

"I'd like you to write down—in no particular order—the people you spend the most time with. Come up with ten if you can. Just jot down their first names in the column on the left."

With that, Simon stood up and walked to the cockpit. I could hear him greet the pilot and co-pilot, and the murmur of conversation.

I looked out the window, across the tarmac. *Is this crazy?* I wondered, not for the first time that day. Then I thought of Jasmine. *Embrace it*, she'd said.

I looked down at the paper in my hand. Ten people. Let's see. There was Jasmine, of course. And her brother—he and I had become close, and I saw him often. I also had two close friends from college who lived in the city, and we had drinks once a week, and an ongoing text chat. They were the guys I knew I could simply call anytime, with no reason.

That was four. Who else? I remember the couples we had dinner with regularly, and I jotted them down. That gave me ten.

I looked over the list. There it was: my ten closest friends. It was strange to write them down like that—to commit it to paper—but it was true. Those were the people I spent the most time with, the people I naturally fit with. We vacationed together, ate together, laughed together. When the going got tough, we supported each other.

I realized they all would have been at my father's funeral if I'd told them about it, and I felt a flush of shame.

There was a small jolt as the plane began to move, and I looked up to see that Simon had returned to his seat.

"Buckle up," he said with a smile. "You've got quite a journey ahead of you."

* * *

Moments later, we were in the air.

Simon busied himself with some paperwork. I simply looked out the window. There was, I realized, nothing for me to do. I felt like I'd just stepped off some metaphysical cliff. Now I just had to wait to find out what waited at the bottom.

An unexpected feeling of relief washed over me. I was committed. There was no going back. For better or for worse, this was the path I was taking.

"How did you fare with your list?" Simon asked.

"Done," I said. "Ten names. Very mysterious," I added, with a smile. I was beginning to relax. As crazy as this all was, here I was in a private *jet*. I knew if Jas were here, she'd be elbowing me, saying, *Smile, Ethan. This is amazing. Embrace it.*

Simon leaned forward.

"Now, for each name on the list, I'd like you to write down how much they earn in a year."

"Seriously?"

"You might have to guess at some—we don't always like to talk about money in our culture—but do your best."

I scanned the list. Some were easy—I knew what Jasmine's income was down to the penny. Especially recently, when every penny seemed to matter. I wrote it down in the right column beside her name.

I could make accurate guesses about my two friends from school. We'd talked about money enough, and I jotted down from my memory what they earned.

Jasmine's brother was an entrepreneur like me, but I had a ballpark guess on his income from our late night, scotch-fueled business conversations. I listed it in the column as well.

Our "couple" friends were trickier. We didn't really talk about money—at least not so overtly. But I knew about their homes and their cars, and I knew about their jobs. I was pretty confident I could get within 10-15%, so I wrote those numbers down as well.

So there it was. All the people closest to me and their incomes. *How weird is this?*

"While you're at it," Simon said. "Write your income down as well."

I wrote the number at the bottom of the page.

"Now, I want you to take the average of the ten incomes you wrote down."

I added up the numbers and divided by ten.

Whoa.

Simon saw the expression on my face and chuckled. "Remarkable, yes? I've never seen it come out any other way."

I looked at the list. My income wasn't *exactly* the same as the average I'd calculated, but it was so close that it was shocking.

"I could ask you to do the same thing for your body fat," he said, "or any number of other things, and you'd see a similar result."

I thought of my friends. They were certainly different shapes and sizes. But we weren't *that* different.

I could feel Simon watching me.

"Okay," I said. "So I hang out with people similar to me. Nothing odd about that."

"Not at all. It's commonplace. But have you ever wondered *why* you're so similar?"

I hadn't. "I guess that we're similar, so we tend to spend time together. We fit."

"You're partly right," Simon said. "But let me ask you this. Do you think you spend time together because you're similar?" he tapped a finger on the sheet of paper. "Or are you similar because you spend time together?"

"Wait. What?"

Simon smiled. "I know it feels like a chicken and egg scenario," he said. "But there's a deep truth here that's important to understand for our time together."

"I'm all ears." And I really was. Simon's little exercise had my curiosity muscles twitching.

"We tend to feel like we make conscious decisions about our lives," Simon said. "We make decisions. We take action. We get results. We shape our destinies."

"That's certainly how I feel. I think every entrepreneur does."

"We are indeed agents of change, Ethan. The successful people of the world do make decisions and consciously shape their futures. What we don't realize is that *subconsciously*, there are powerful forces at work that affect how we think and act."

"What kind of forces?"

"We're being subtly shaped by the world around us all the time," Simon said. "Just being here in this jet, for example, is changing you the way you think. It might make you more motivated. Or it might make you insecure. It might make you more confident. The point is that it's having an effect below the level of your awareness. It's what we call the *Influence Effect*. It means that, even without you being aware of it, your environment is constantly changing you."

I looked down at the list of names in my hand. "And that's why my income is so close to the average of my friends?" I asked.

"Precisely," Simon said. "They're a type of influence. In fact, the most powerful form of the Influence Effect comes from the people around you."

"Like peer pressure?"

"Peer pressure is an overt form of the Influence Effect," Simon said, "but the real effect is much deeper, and it's invisible to almost everyone."

"But I still feel like I make my own choices. I certainly didn't collaborate with all my friends and agree to make the same income each year."

"No, you didn't conspire with your peers," Simon said with a smile. "But you were perhaps conspired *against*. The Influence Effect goes back much farther than your peers, Ethan. Back to the early days of humanity, to a time when the people around you weren't just your friends or family. They were your ticket to survival.

"Back then, it took enormous effort, persistence, and good fortune just to live long enough to reproduce. Early humans drew on an advantage that many species did—they banded together in *tribes*. You can call them packs, groups, or families if you want, but they all served the same purpose: to help us survive."

"So the people in the tribe influenced each other?"

"It's more nuanced than that. Belonging to a tribe offered survival advantages. But in order to belong to a tribe, you needed to fit in. You had to be *like* the tribe in order to be *liked* by the tribe.

"Now, hundreds of thousands of years later, we still have that drive. Deep in our primitive brain, the neural circuits that push us to fit into the tribe around us are still firing as if every day is a fight for survival."

A light bulb began to glow in my mind.

"Is that why people dress alike?"

"Absolutely. How you dress, what you buy, how you eat—those things are all influenced by those around you. But more importantly, so is how you *think*. What you believe is possible, what you believe you are capable of, these things are dictated by the Influence Effect.

You are, whether you like it or not, a product of your tribe."

Just then, the pilot's voice came over the cabin speaker.

Gentlemen, the voice said, *we're just a few minutes out. If you'd like to buckle up, we'll get you on the ground and on your way.*

The plane banked and I leaned to look out the window.

Wow. Beneath me, a beautiful island sat in a twinkling turquoise sea.

Rimmed by beaches, covered in a thick jungle canopy, it seemed deserted, except for the furthest tip of the island where a short landing strip had been carved from the jungle. Offshore, I could see the light colors of sand and coral reefs just off the beach, then a deepening blue further out as the water deepened.

It was stunning.

Simon motioned at the island through the window. "It's easy to think you're an island, Ethan," he said. "In fact, you've been *trained* to think that way. By your parents, by the media, by your peers. Our whole culture promotes the idea that we're all rugged individualists, making our way alone, independent. We were explorers, then rugged pioneers, then self-made men, then entrepreneurs. Our whole history has been told in a way that casts us as self-sufficient lone wolves.

"It's simply not true. No man is an island. In fact," he nodded out the window. "No island is just an island. What looks like a lone island in the sea is constantly being transformed by the Influence Effect. That beach is shaped by the waves. That beautiful lagoon is the remains of an ancient volcano. Like the island, you're constantly being shaped by forces around you. And the greatest of those forces is *people.*"

I buckled my seatbelt as the plane began to descend. *Was it true?* Were the people around me truly that influential? I turned the idea over in my mind. Somehow, it seemed *right.*

Moments later, the plane touched down with a soft *thump.*

"Here we are," Simon said.

I looked down at the list of names in my hand. What did it all mean? Was I supposed to abandon my friends and family if I wanted to succeed?

Simon followed my gaze. He pointed at the numbers. "It's right there in the numbers. The people you're closest to change how you think, what you believe, and how you act. Their influence can be an anchor that holds you back, or sail that moves you forward; the choice is yours."

There was a click, and the door of the plane opened. Bright sunlight poured through the opening. A moment later, a wave of hot, humid air blew across us. I could smell the sea.

"So…let me get this straight. The people I spend time with are actually influencing my income?"

"They're doing more than that, Ethan," he said. He picked up his briefcase and stood up. "They're determining your destiny."

And with that, stepped past me and walked to the door.

"Wait," I said. "Where did you learn this from? The Influence Effect—who told you about it?"

Simon paused in the door of the jet, as if lost in thought. After a moment, he turned back to me.

"Your father," he said.

THE FIRST EFFECT

SUMMARY

THE INFLUENCE EFFECT

Your destiny is shaped by those around you

- You're being subtly and powerfully shaped by your environment—often below the level of your awareness.

- The most powerful of environmental influences is the people around you.

- The people you choose to surround yourself with can be an anchor that holds you back, or sail that moves you forward; the choice is yours.

CHAPTER 4
THE TRIBE

My father?

There was little time to process what Simon had said. As he disappeared through the door, I grabbed my bag and followed him into a blast of tropical heat and humidity.

I squinted in the sun as my eyes adjusted. As I'd seen from the plane, the runway had been carved from the jungle. To one side of the airstrip was a wall of green forest. To the other, a turquoise sea twinkling in the sun. In the distance, a conical mountain loomed over the jungle.

Simon was already down the stairs. He placed a worn fedora-style hat on his bald head and strode across the tarmac toward a waiting jeep.

* * *

Our driver greeted Simon like an old friend and gave me a firm handshake. We hopped aboard the jeep and left the runway, following a dirt road that disappeared into the dark of the jungle.

We sputtered along the path, apparently in no rush, the driver chatting amiably with Simon, occasionally pointing into the deep green around us.

"You'll have to adjust your watch to island time," Simon said with a smile. "Things tend to move a little more slowly here."

I peered into the jungle alongside the road. Vines hung from enormous trees. Colorful birds flitted from branches. Somewhere deeper, I heard the chattering cries of something wild. Monkeys?

I felt a pang of anxiety. Should I really be here? Traipsing around some tropical island while my company slowly sank into the sea back home?

I looked over at Simon. His formal manner seemed out of place here, yet he was more relaxed than I'd seen him before. Was that the Influence Effect at work? *Maybe a little island time will help*, I thought, and I resolved to make the most of the day.

"The exercise from the plane," I said to Simon. "Is it just my closest friends that create the Influence Effect?"

"I used your closest friends because they're a particularly effective example," Simon said. "But the Influence Effect isn't just your friends and family. It spans your whole life. The people around you *change* you. In subtle ways, yes, but those changes compound over time. They stack up to change the trajectory of your life."

"Is it all a function of time? The more time I spend with someone, the more influence?"

Simon thought. "Great question. Time is certainly a factor. But influence can also be created by *intensity*."

"How so?"

"A great example would be people who go through a highly emotional experience together. Think of troops in battle. Even a short period of time together bonds them very closely. In those cases, the Influence Effect can be very strong."

"Am I going to have to enlist to harness the effect?" I asked, with a smile.

"Nothing that dramatic. You simply need to make more conscious choices about the people you allow to influence you."

Hmm. I'd never thought about the people around me as being particularly conscious choices. In my mind, I had personal relationships and professional relationships—everything fell into one of those two buckets.

Was there anyone in my life that I'd consciously chosen because of their influence? I didn't think so. I'd chosen Jasmine for love—I knew that. I had hired the people in the business for their skills. And my friends? Well, I suppose they were just people I enjoyed. Had I been conscious in choosing them? I wasn't sure.

My thoughts drifted to other people in my life. Now that I was seeing things through a different lens, I began to wonder: *were they influencing me?* I had one friend who loved to exercise—we often did things outdoors together, like hiking. Another friend was different. He loved bars and restaurants and movies. When I was with him, I realized, I had fun, but I tended to make different choices; not all of them were great ones.

Then it hit me: was I going to be asked to change *friends?* I couldn't imagine it. Whatever it was I was here to do, I was determined that abandoning my friends was not going to be part of it.

The jeep emerged from the jungle into a large clearing on the edge of the ocean. The clearing was like a movie scene—coconut palms shot into the sky, casting shade over a series of beautiful thatch-roofed buildings that fit perfectly against the surroundings. No wonder I hadn't seen anything from the air.

The driver stopped the jeep in front of the largest of the buildings. It was an enormous circular lodge made of a beautiful dark wood. A set of stairs swept up to a long shaded porch.

"Here we are," Simon said.

We unloaded our bags, but I still felt a nagging question about the influence effect.

"Simon," I said. "I understand what you've been telling me about the Influence Effect. It makes a lot of sense. I can already see how my life has been shaped by the people around me."

Simon took off his fedora and wiped the sweat from his brow.

"What I'm wondering," I continued, "is how I put that to work. Am I supposed to get rid of my friends and family that don't... well, serve me?"

"Another great question," Simon said. "And the answer is no. I don't expect you to abandon your friends and family, unless they are truly a negative influence."

I ignored the voice in my head that said, *you already tried that with your father.*

"That's good," I said.

Simon slipped his fedora back on, and then picked up his suitcase.

"Rather than abandon your tribe, Ethan," he said, "the plan is to expose you to a new one."

And with that, he marched up the stairs and beneath the thatched roof of the huge building.

* * *

I followed Simon through a door into a large open room with a high roof, crisscrossed with dark hand-hewn beams. The entire ocean-facing side of the building was open to the beach and sea, and I could smell the salt breeze.

There were perhaps forty people milling about the room in groups ranging in size from pairs to four or five. Conversation filled the air, punctuated by bursts of laughter. The air was almost electric—a hum of activity filled the space.

It was clear that everyone in this room knew each other, and I scanned the room, feeling out of place. At first, I recognized no one, then I caught sight of one familiar face, then others: they were the men from my father's funeral. They were casually dressed in shorts and comfortable shirts rather than black suits, but there was no mistaking them.

Beyond the wooden railings and the low thatched roofline, I could see an unbroken stretch of perfect sand beach. Wind rustled the fronds of the palms along the shore. Inland, in the distance, the dark rock face of the mountain rose above the jungle.

I realized that the room had grown silent. I pulled my gaze away from the beach and realized that everyone in the room had stopped speaking. They were all watching me, nodding, smiling.

I could hear the gentle lapping of waves on the shore. In the distance, the cry of a seabird.

"What is this?" I asked Simon, under my breath.

"Ethan," Simon said with a smile. "Welcome to the Tribe of Millionaires."

* * *

The rest of the afternoon passed in a blur. Someone put a drink in my hand, and Simon and I moved through the room, with Simon greeting each person warmly and introducing me.

For the first few handshakes I tried to remember names, but eventually there were just too many, and I simply tried my best to keep up.

What stuck with me long after the names had vanished was the way in which so many of the men greeted me. "It's so nice to finally meet you, Ethan," was a phrase that I heard over and over. It was if they all knew me somehow. It was unsettling, but, I had to admit, it was also comforting.

I paid special attention to the men I recognized from my father's funeral. Like Simon, each seemed fit and healthy, but also gave off an almost palpable energy—a strange mixture of confidence without arrogance, contentment without complacency. Each was different, yet they were alike in that I'd never met anyone quite like them.

After introductions, Simon gave me a tour of the compound and showed me to my room—a basic but beautiful hut perched at the edge of where the jungle met the beach.

"Freshen up," he said. "Relax a little, get your bearings. Then meet back at the main lodge for dinner."

I thanked Simon, then dropped my bags inside. I showered, then sat on the porch of my hut, staring at the sea.

What was I doing here? Was this really the right choice?

I heard Jasmine's voice in my head: *Embrace it, Ethan.*

She was right. I stood up and headed for the lodge.

* * *

I met Simon back in the large room, where he offered me a drink. We sat looking out at the beach as people began to drift into the room.

"You told me earlier that you learned the Influence Effect from my father," I said after we'd sat in silence for a few minutes. "Where did he learn it?"

"Your father invented it," he said. Then he laughed, "That's not true, actually. No one invented the Influence Effect. It's like gravity. It's always been here and always will. You can't escape it, only use it to your advantage."

"But my father taught it to you?"

"Like the apple falling on Newton's head, your father was just the first person to notice and articulate it. He taught it first to me. Then, together we taught it to others."

That just doesn't sound like my father. But, then again, how much did I really know about him?

As the sun set, we moved off the thatched veranda and down to the beach where long tables had been set in the sand. Tall bamboo torches flickered in the ocean breeze.

We served ourselves from platters of fresh seafood heaped over rice, and strange but delicious vegetables that I assumed must be local to the island.

I leaned over to Simon. "I never thought I'd say this, but I'd like to ask you more about my father."

He nodded. "All in good time, Ethan. Your father was a great man. Extraordinary. It would be my privilege. But tonight," he said, motioning at the table around us, "just relax. Enjoy. You have a lot ahead of you."

Extraordinary? My father? A lot ahead of me? One mystery after another.

Embrace it, Jas said, in my inner ear.

As we ate, a full moon rose above the mountain. The waves, smaller now in the night, splashed smoothly against the sand.

As the buzz of conversation and laughter continued long into the night, I looked up at the stars overhead.

Embrace it.

For the first time in as long as I could remember, I felt something inside me. A long-forgotten sensation.

It was just a glimmer, a beginning. But I could swear that it was a sense of peace.

CHAPTER 5
THE SECOND EFFECT

I awoke disoriented, reaching for an alarm clock that wasn't there.

A strange jungle cry chattered in the distance. A wave crashed on the beach.

The island.

It all came flooding back. Simon. The flight. The beautiful island, the jeep ride. And the night of warm conversation.

And that feeling—that sense of being at peace. At being *home.* Was it all real?

As dinner had carried on into the night, I'd eventually felt the day catching up to me. Simon had noticed my head nodding, and we excused ourselves. That path back to my "room" had been lit with torches, and within minutes, I was in the comfortable bed with a pale mosquito net hung over me like a canopy. It was beautiful.

Now, in the morning sunlight, I stared up at the shimmering canopy. *Jasmine would love this.*

Damn! I'd forgotten to let her know I'd arrived safely. She'd be worried sick.

I reached for my phone and switched it on. *Had I really just gone an entire day without looking at my phone?* It was hard to believe.

I dashed off a quick message to Jas, but it was no sooner sent when a barrage of inbound messages began.

The last of my peaceful feeling vanished. Here was reality finding me even here on a remote island. One message was flagged with a subject line in ALL CAPS. I sighed, and clicked on it.

It was from Andrew, my operations manager, and probably the person I spent the most time with. In our small office, he did a little of everything, but he'd insisted on the title of VP of Operations—which I'd given him. To me, it was little more than what was printed on a business card, but it was important to Andrew.

I knew when I hired him that I wasn't a detail guy. It was a strength, in a way, but also a weakness, and I needed someone who could focus on those things.

Lately, though, Andrew's attention to detail had become almost pathological. The more we moved into crisis mode at the office, the more I needed him to be flexible, but as things got trickier, he became more entrenched in his procedures.

I knew that it was beginning to bother me, but this morning I realized I was more than bothered. I was angry at his message. Even though he was simply keeping me up to date, I found myself feeling resentful that I couldn't seem to escape, even here.

As I considered how to reply, I heard a noise on the porch of my hut. A small, white envelope slid under the door.

I climbed out of bed and retrieved it. It carried the usual T o M embossing that I'd become familiar with. *Tribe of Millionaires.* Only then did it hit me that I'd just met the actual Tribe.

I opened the envelope. There were two pieces of paper inside. The first was a handwritten note:

Good morning Ethan,

See you for breakfast at 9. Dress for hiking.
We have ground to cover.

- Vikram

Vikram. I'd met him the night before. He was one of the men who'd carried my father's casket, and was, in many ways, Simon's opposite. He was short, with dark skin and thick, bristly grey hair. A chiropractor, if my overloaded memory was correct.

The second piece of paper was thick white cardstock, printed with the following:

THE INFLUENCE EFFECT

Your destiny is shaped by those around you

I thought back to the exercise on the jet. It was a compelling argument. One, apparently, that Simon had learned from my father.

I dropped the card on the dresser, got dressed, and headed to breakfast.

* * *

Vikram was exactly as I remembered him from the night before, short and incredibly warm, with a near-constant smile.

He gave me a firm handshake. "How are you feeling? Overwhelmed?"

"Exhilarated, I think." It was true. Despite the challenges awaiting me at home, I felt more optimistic than I had in ages. "Thank you for the reminder of the Influence Effect. I've been thinking about it almost constantly."

"It's a compelling idea," Vikram said, beaming. "And, I can assure you, it's quite true. I'm living proof. If it wasn't for your father's theories, I might be in a very different—and much worse—place."

There it was again, this mention of my father. I was curious to know more, but for the rest of breakfast, we were interrupted almost constantly by a stream of other tribe members who arrived steadily for breakfast.

It was nearly an hour before we wrapped up, and I followed Vikram outside. "I hope you like walking," he said. "We do a lot of it here."

He led me away from the main lodge, onto a path that meandered away from the beach, and into the jungle. The green canopy was alive with the sounds of birds and other chattering creatures.

"Yesterday," he began, "did Simon ask you to identify the people you spend the most time with?"

"He did. It was very insightful."

"Indeed," he smiled. "I did the same exercise once, long ago. The Influence Effect states that you are a product of your environment, in particular the people around you. Choose the wrong people, and they hold you back from your potential. Choose the right ones, and they help you to reach it."

"I think I've become a believer in just a few hours," I joked.

"Good," Vikram said. "Very good. But my job today is to tell you what the Influence Effect *doesn't* reveal."

"What it doesn't?"

"Yes. It teaches us that the people around us *change* us. But it doesn't reveal the extent. It doesn't tell us just how *much*. That's my job."

Vikram paused on the jungle trail. He pointed into the canopy to where a group of monkeys swung nimbly across a series of thick vines.

"I'm a chiropractor," Vikram said, "so I deal with the nervous system. Your body contains a vast network that underlies everything else. It's that network that controls your organs, maintains your health, and allows you to run, jump, breathe, and," he smiled and motioned to me, "have a conversation."

Vikram was incredibly personable. I don't think I'd ever met someone who made me feel more immediately comfortable.

"Your nervous system," Vikram continued, "is simply a collection of connections. Like those vines allow the monkeys to connect, your nerves allow your various body parts and functions to communicate with each other. When that network works well, it's a great boost to the system. But take away those vines," he said, "and the monkeys would have a tougher time getting around.

"The people around you are like a network, too," he continued. "And the number and quality of those people affects *your* system— your ability to 'get around'." He smiled.

"Makes sense," I said. "That's the Influence Effect."

"Yes," he said. "But there's more to it. Do you have a phone?" He asked.

"Of course."

"I imagine you use it a lot," he said.

"Probably more than I should," I admitted. "But it's hard to imagine life without it."

"It's an incredibly useful tool," Vikram said. "But let me ask you this. If you were the *only* person with a phone, how useful would it be?"

I didn't have to think long to answer. "Not at all. I couldn't message or call anyone. It would be pointless."

"Exactly. What if just one more person had a phone—say, your wife, for example."

"That would be better, but certainly nowhere near as valuable as if everyone I knew had one."

"Precisely," Vikram said. "The more people in your network who have a phone, the more valuable the connection is. In telecommunication technology, there's a law for that. It's called Metcalfe's Law. It says that the effect of the network grows in proportion to the square of the number of connected users."

"Wait…what?"

Vikram chuckled. "That's a fancy way of saying that effect of the network doesn't just go up in a straight line. It gets proportionally more valuable. In our tribe, we have a similar rule. It's called the Multiplier Effect. It says that whatever you do alone, you can do far better in a group."

I thought about this. "So. When I'm alone, I'm like a single cell phone. I'm not that useful."

"Yes!" Vikram said. "And as you surround yourself with more people, your ability to make things happen is *multiplied*."

"Hmm. Is this true of any group?"

"Ah… excellent question. No. The Influence Effect is always at work. A broken phone doesn't add to the value of a network. It may even decrease the value. Choosing to surround yourself with the right people is still critical. What I'm telling you is that those people don't just add to your efforts. They *multiply* them. The right group *compounds*. The wrong one, however, just *confounds*. It gets in the way."

We came to a fork in the trail. Ahead of us, the trail began to climb slightly, and I guessed we were getting closer to the large mountain at the island's center.

Vikram followed the branch to the left.

"We'll be taking that trail later this week," he said. "For now, we can follow this back."

"What's happening later this week?" I asked.

"Ah. A special event," Vikram replied, then said nothing more.

Fine, I thought. *Keep your secrets.*

A pair of monkeys scampered through the trees overhead, and I mulled over what Vikram had said about the Multiplier Effect.

"I'm not saying I don't believe you," I said to Vikram. "But how exactly does the Multiplier Effect work? I mean, phones are one thing, but a telecommunications network is a lot different than a group of people."

"It is indeed," Vikram said. "But the effect still holds. In the context of people, however, the effect is due to some very specific reasons."

"What are they?"

Vikram was silent for a moment. "When I joined the Tribe of Millionaires," he said, "I was struggling in my chiropractic practice. I knew intuitively that being alone wasn't helping, but I didn't realize the true value of the people around me until I experienced it. After I joined the tribe, my business literally tripled in just a few months."

"Really?" *I could certainly use some tripling*, I thought.

"Really," he said. "All I had to do was to let the network work. The Multiplier Effect took care of it from there."

"I'd love to hear a bit more," I said. "How did the effect really work?"

"Funny you should ask," he replied. "I always feel like the best way to learn something is to experience it. I understand from Simon that you're in some difficulty with your business."

Have these guys been talking about me? I wondered. *How does Simon even know that?*

"You could say that," I said.

"I hope you don't mind," he said, "But I've made arrangements with the tribe. With your permission, I'd like to show you the Multiplier Effect in action."

* * *

When we arrived back at the main lodge, there were a dozen or so tribe members gathered on the porch. Several were sweaty from morning runs. Another group carried diving masks and fins. Clearly, this was an active bunch.

"Good morning everyone," Vikram said. "Thanks for coming out. You all met Ethan last night. I've asked you here today to help us bring a little tribal magic to Ethan's business."

The assembled members took seats around tables. Vikram motioned to me. "Ethan, why don't you give us a quick summary of your business and the challenges you're facing."

"Uh...sure." I stood awkwardly in front of the group. I looked out over their heads at the ocean and tried to figure out where to begin. I felt like I was at some sort of support group. *Hello, my name is Ethan and I'm a failure.*

I felt strangely nervous. My palms began to sweat. "I... uh... I," I stammered. The group waited expectantly. Finally, I blurted out in one rapid stream, "We're-out-of-money-and-nothing-is-working-and-it's-all-a-failure."

My revelation was met with silence.

One man leaned back in his chair. Tall and stocky, he was built like a retired linebacker. His sheer physicality seemed to grant him a certain authority, and I recognized him immediately. Like Vikram, he was one of the pallbearers from my father's funeral.

"Well," he said in a gruff voice, "You nailed the quick part."

I felt my face redden.

Vikram rescued me. "Ethan," he said, "why don't you tell Terry and the rest of us a little more about your business itself?"

Terry. Vikram. Simon. I was slowly getting to know those closest to my father.

"Sure," I said. I took a deep breath and tried to center myself. "We make software that allows fitness and wellness centers to offer rewards for regular attendance."

"What kind of rewards?" It was the linebacker-sized man again, Terry.

I began to relax. I was in pitch mode now. *This I can do*, I thought. "Gyms, yoga studios, and the like—they work on a membership system. The customer pays a monthly fee and uses the service as much or as little as they want."

I noticed heads nodding around me. I began to settle in.

"The problem is that attrition is high. People sign up at the start of a new year, for example, and use the gym for a week or two, then end up canceling their membership early, or not renewing."

"So where do you fit in?" one man asked.

"We combine retail and consumer service partners with an app that tracks attendance. When people work out, they get reward points that they can use at businesses in the area, or with online vendors."

"How do you get paid?" Terry asked.

"We get a small monthly fee for every active user that uses the system."

"In essence," another man said, "you get a piece of the monthly membership in exchange for increasing customer retention."

"Exactly." *Wow*, I thought. *These guys are sharp.* When I pitched this idea to gyms and studios, it was always an uphill battle. I often had to start by explaining the basic premise of customer retention, period.

I was, I realized, in a room of very different people. *The Influence Effect,* I thought.

"So what's the problem?" Terry asked.

I refocused. "Well, it took a lot longer than we thought to create the relationships with the neighborhood partners. But we eventually got a test market up and running."

"That doesn't sound like a problem."

It is if you're broke, I thought. But I remembered Vikram's story. *Let the network work.* Maybe he was right. The delay was just that—a delay. And, now that I was facing it down, I knew it was more of an *excuse.*

I took a deep breath. "The real problem," I said, "is that it hasn't been working."

No one spoke.

This was the first time I'd admitted it aloud. In fact, I hadn't told *anyone* this. Not even Jasmine. *Especially* Jasmine. Some of my more astute team members could tell the results weren't meeting targets, but I kept up a game face. *People just have to learn, to change their habits,* I'd say. But privately I thought, *I'm trying to build a company based on the idea that habit change is hard. And now I've just bet everything on yet another habit change.*

I looked out at the ocean. I felt like I was taking a deep dive.

I turned back to the group and explained how our system just didn't seem to be leading to increased attendance or retention. All it did was grant rewards to the same people who would be going to the gym anyway.

"Ah," Terry said. I could hear some hushed mumble and murmurs among the group members.

"Ethan," Terry said, "We have a process for these types of things. Would you be open to trying it out?"

"If it'll help, I'll try anything."

For the next twenty minutes, Vikram guided the group through a discussion based on my business. It was clear they'd all been through the process before, but for me, it was a revelation. It began with a clear statement of the goal, which Vikram wrote on a whiteboard he'd retrieved from a corner of the room:

To generate possible solutions for Ethan's business problem

"Okay, Vikram said, "Ten minutes, groups of six."

There was a grinding of chairs and tables and the group quickly broke into three smaller groups. Vikram and I stood aside, as the groups immediately dove into animated conversation.

"What are they doing?" I asked Vikram.

"They're generating ideas," he said. "Brainstorming."

"Don't they need me to be involved?"

"You will be," he said. "But not yet. You're too close to the problem. For now, you have to let the network work." There was that phrase again.

After ten minutes, Vikram stopped the groups. "Okay," he said. "What have you got?"

A spokesperson from each group got up and began to list off ideas. Vikram jotted them down in point form on the board. They covered a wide range of ideas from *quit* to *get better/more partners*. Most I understood immediately, and in fact, had been discussed already back in the office. A couple jumped out at me, however, and I pointed at them.

"Could I get some more on these?"

Vikram read the first one. "*Take the same infrastructure to a different industry.*"

A short man with glasses from the second group raised his hand and stood up. "Hi, Ethan. I'm Davis. That was me."

I recognized the man as another of the pallbearers from my father's funeral.

"You're rewarding people for something," Davis continued. "I see that. It's a great idea. But if people *don't* go to the gym, nothing really happens. There's no penalty."

"That's true," I said.

"So your business is about the carrot, not the stick."

That's an intriguing way to look at it, I thought.

"So what if you brought your idea to a different industry—one where there was already more incentive to do the behavior? Perhaps one where there was already a stick, and you could add your carrot?"

"Like what?"

"Well. I'm in multi-family real estate," Davis said. "Apartment buildings, condominiums. I was thinking maybe your system could be used to reward people for paying rent on time, reporting maintenance issues promptly, things like that. Those things do have a penalty for not doing them—either in the form of late fees, or inconveniences, or repair costs—but people still struggle to take action. If I could reward my tenants for the right behavior, that might be helpful for everyone."

I had never even considered switching industries. We were so locked into our idea that it wasn't even on our radar. It would mean a lot of effort, but—could it work?

"Thanks, Davis," I said. "I never thought of that. We already have the partners in place. I guess it could be done."

Davis nodded and sat down.

"How about this one?" Vikram read off the second one I'd asked about. "*What if you paid people in cash to work out?*"

A different man stood up—yet another of my father's pallbearers. "G'day mate," he said, in a thick Australian accent. "I'm Bruce."

Really? I thought. *An Australian named Bruce?*

Simon, Vikram, Terry, Davis, and now *Bruce*. I tried to keep track of the names.

"This one came up in our discussion," Bruce continued, "and we thought it was worth considering, too."

"How would it work?" I asked him. "I mean, we can't even pay our bills right now."

"You've already got a network of partners, right? The people that provide the rewards in exchange for exposure?"

"Yes. Hundreds, in fact. It was the hardest part—other than making money, that is."

"We actually did some additional brainstorming on this one," Bruce said. "We went a little deeper. We have a list here that you can look at, but here are a couple of possibilities."

Another man handed him a sheet of paper, and Bruce read from it.

"One was what we called 'micro-sponsorship'. Get people to post to social media or use branded swag when they work out, in exchange for being paid for each gym visit. It's basically like taking amateurs, and 'sponsoring' them to work out as if they were athletes. The network you've created to give rewards could provide cash rewards instead for people becoming walking billboards."

Bruce scanned the list.

"Another was a to create a secondary marketplace to convert the rewards you've set up back into cash. I might not want my rewards points for the local sandwich shop, but if there's a way to convert them to cash, I might be more motivated. It's been done before in other reward systems."

I'd never considered it. It was a complete reversal. *Pay* people to exercise? In cash? Was it even possible?

As I stood in amazement. Bruce spoke again. "I have a contact in the credit card reward business. I'm almost sure he can connect you with someone who could help you."

"Likewise," Davis said. "Plenty of contacts in real estate. In fact, I'm personally interested. If you want to discuss further, just let me know."

* * *

After a few more questions and some discussion, we ended the session. As the men drifted off in twos and threes, I was astonished by how nonchalant they seemed. As if completely transforming someone's entire business was just all in a morning's work.

"Well?" Vikram said. "Was that helpful?"

"Wow." I paused, almost breathless. "That... it... this could be worth a fortune to my business."

"That's what the Multiplier Effect teaches us," Vikram said. "The right kind of influence doesn't just add to your efforts. It compounds over time. It *multiplies*."

"I'm still not sure I really understand what just happened," I said.

"You're seeing very specific elements of the multiplier effect," Vikram said. "When Terry asked you about your business, he was digging for *clarity*. To push you to more clearly define your situation."

"Well, he succeeded," I said. "That was the first time I've ever stated the *real* problem we're facing."

"Excellent," Vikram said. "Then, when the group began to bat ideas around, they were leveraging off each other, increasing the *creativity* of the group as a whole. One idea would spring from another, creating new ideas that simply wouldn't come up without that group dynamic."

Vikram pointed at the two ideas circled on the whiteboard. "Then, once you'd focused in on a possible opportunity, the group was able to provide you with *connectivity*—people in their network that you could tap into to test the idea or put it into action."

"Clarity, creativity, connectivity," he summarized. "Those are the elements that multiply what you can do alone. You simply cannot get the same results on your own in those areas."

"The Multiplier Effect," I said, in awe.

"The Multiplier Effect," Vikram said, smiling.

* * *

I spent the next hour back in my *hut*—although hut was hardly the right word, I realized—furiously scribbling notes. It was like my brain had been split open, my mind widened, and ideas were pouring out.

This could work, I thought. *We could pivot. Change directions. We could stay alive.*

No, I thought.

More than stay alive. We could thrive.

We could *multiply*.

THE SECOND EFFECT
SUMMARY

THE MULTIPLIER EFFECT

The right group of people compounds your efforts.

- The right group doesn't just add to your efforts—it *multiplies* them.

- Multiplication happens through *creativity*, *clarity*, and *connectivity.*

- The best groups don't make decisions for you. They give you the raw ideas for more options, the clarity to choose the best course, and the connections to help execute faster and better.

- The wrong group *confounds.* The right group *compounds.*

CHAPTER 6
THE THIRD EFFECT

I awoke the next morning to another envelope under the door. As with the previous day, it contained two pieces of paper.

The first was a note:

Ethan,
Pier. 9AM.
-Terry

I remembered Terry from the brainstorming session the day before. He was the gruff, linebacker-sized man. Apparently, he was also a man of few words.

The second piece of paper was another card embossed with the T o M logo:

THE MULTIPLIER EFFECT

The right group of people compounds your efforts.

Again, I thought back to the previous day's session, and the incredible insight the group had shown for my business. *I should follow up with Davis and Bruce*, I thought. Their suggestions were so creative, and after thinking it through the night before, I had a way in which I could perhaps use both their ideas.

I picked up my phone to message both men, since they had given me their contact information after the session. Immediately, however, my attention was captured by multiple messages from Andrew at the office.

More ALL CAPS.

More *Urgent Requests.*

More exclamation points. God, how I was coming to hate exclamation points.

To be fair, Andrew wasn't the only one. There were other messages—from other staff, from investors. As I read through them, I felt my optimism slipping away.

Damn it, I thought. *I can't do my job when I'm being hounded by a group of—*

I paused. *A group.* I looked at the card Terry had left. *The right group of people compounds your efforts.*

The bedside table was covered in paper from my previous night's work. I began to pick through the sheets, tossing aside them this way and that, trying to find what I wanted.

"There you are," I said to the empty room.

In my hand, I held the matching card Vikram had left me. *The Influence Effect: Your destiny is shaped by those around you.*

I looked at the two cards, then down at my phone with its list of urgent messages.

I sat down and began to type.

Five minutes later, I was out the door.

* * *

After a quick breakfast in the main building, I hurried down to the beach where a long wooden pier jutted into the turquoise water.

Several small boats and a pair of jet skis were tethered in the shallows. At the end of the dock, I could see men gathered around a large covered boat. Even from a distance, I recognized the towering figure of Terry, who loomed a few inches over everyone else.

I walked quickly down the pier. Terry nodded at me.

"You're late," he said.

"Sorry," I said. "I had a few things to sort out at the office."

Terry looked as if he might say something, but instead, he handed me a mesh bag. In it were a set of fins, a dive mask, and some other gear.

"Ever been scuba diving?" he asked.

"No," I said. "I've been in the water a lot. I'm a good swimmer. I can snorkel. But I've never actually been diving."

"You're in for a treat," he said. "Climb aboard." He turned to the other two men. "Let's do this." One of them hopped aboard and started the boat's engines. The other began to untie the dock lines.

I grabbed the railing and stepped aboard.

* * *

Moments later, the boat was cruising smoothly over the sea. I turned my face to the sun and felt the salt breeze in my hair. *Ahh.* More than ever, I was sure I'd done the right thing before I'd left my room.

I turned to Terry. He stood at the rail of the boat, staring out at the sea. It was difficult to tell how old he was, but I knew one thing for certain: he was *fit.* He was tall, muscular, tanned. He had to be in his fifties, yet he looked as strong as a twenty-year-old.

"I'm sorry I was late," I said to him. "I got your card this morning, and I guess it came at the perfect time. I wanted to put the lessons to work—the Influence Effect and the Multiplier Effect. So I did. Or, at least I *think* I did."

"How so?" Terry asked.

"As you know, we're in a bit of a crisis in the business. I'm trying to lead us through it, and I think that being here can help. But every time I feel myself getting the clarity and the headspace to see things from a higher level, I get jerked back to reality by details at work. My team is constantly on me."

Terry nodded but said nothing. The boat began to slow, then the captain stopped the engines, and we drifted to a stop in the still water.

"Anyway," I said, "that's why I was late. I told my team I was unavailable for the week. That I understood the situation, and I needed their help so I could lead us through it. I think cutting them off will give me a few days grace to learn from the Tribe."

"That was a good call," Terry said.

"Thanks, I—"

"But," he said, cutting me off with a wave. "That doesn't mean you can be late."

What a hardass, I thought.

Terry looked over the side of the boat, then motioned to me. I leaned over beside him.

Wow. The water was like glass. I could see straight down to a stretch of white, sandy sea floor, dotted with coral outcroppings.

Everywhere I looked there were fish. Fish of all sizes, colors, and shapes. They flitted in and about the coral, some in schools, some alone.

"Incredible," I said.

I watched the fish spin and weave around each other. They never collided. It was like an infinitely complex dance, where every fish somehow knew what to do.

"There are so many different kinds," I said, awestruck.

Terry stepped away from the rail of the boat. "A lot like life, in a way. It isn't one big homogenous pool of like-minded people."

"No kidding." I grinned, but Terry didn't crack a smile.

"You were smart to create some time here this week," he said. "But remember, there will always be those around you who are difficult.

You're always going to have people who make demands on your time, or who don't see things your way."

Terry tossed me a short-sleeved wetsuit.

"That doesn't mean that they're bad people," he continued. "All it means is that you have to manage their presence in your life. This Tribe isn't about isolating yourself from the world, or from people who don't see things your way. It's about learning how those around you affect you, and using that knowledge to everyone's advantage."

The captain barked a quick command. A few moments later, the crew dropped anchor, and Terry began to pull out dive gear. Tanks, regulators, weight belts—they were all things I recognized but had never used.

"Don't worry," Terry said, "I'm going to take you through some short training exercises. I'll show you how all the gear works, get you comfortable, and then we'll do a safe dive in very shallow water."

Terry handed me a mask, and for the next hour, he took me through the basics. We spent some time in the water with just our masks on, looking at the myriad of colored fish. He taught me to clear water from my mask, and how to move safely around the reef, and how I shouldn't touch anything. He watched as I explored. I sensed he was trying to gauge my comfort level.

Back on the boat, we dried off and Terry showed me how to assemble my scuba gear. He attached a set of long hoses to the top of a tank.

"This is your regulator," he said, pointing to a house with a mouthpiece at the end. "It's what you'll breathe from underwater."

I pointed at a second mouthpiece on another hose. "Why are there two?"

"Great question." I could sense Terry's gruff exterior start to slip away a little. He clearly loved the ocean. "This is a spare regulator. We call it an *octopus*."

"So if the other one breaks, I use that one?"

"Yes. But it serves an important second purpose. It's also a spare for your buddy—that's *me*. If my equipment fails or I run out of air, I can breathe from this until we can get safely back to the surface."

Terry attached one end of the regulator to the valve on the tank.

"The octopus brings up the most important part of scuba," he said. "And that's the buddy system. You and I are buddies."

"Aw, shucks," I grinned.

Terry didn't smile.

"In diving," he said, "the buddy system is the one thing, more than anything else, that keeps you alive. It's more than friendship. When we're under the water, we're *responsible* for each other.

"If you're too far away from me," he continued, "and I need this," he grabbed the spare octopus regulator, "it's no good to me if you've wandered off. I need to trust that you have my back."

"Got it," I said.

"And the same applies to me. We're buddies. That's a sacred bond in scuba. We're accountable. If I need you, I have to know you'll show up."

I couldn't tell if that was a jab at my morning lateness, but there was no time to dwell on it. Terry taught me the ins and outs of what he called 'buddy breathing.' It was the process we'd use if something went wrong with our equipment. We practiced it on the deck, went over a few basic hand commands, and then moments later, we were in the water.

* * *

The dive was magical.

I remembered what Terry had told me about the buddy system, and I was sure to keep a close eye on him throughout the dive.

Still, I spent long moments mesmerized by the life around me.

The fish, the coral—it was as if I'd entered another world, a parallel universe where groups of strange creatures interacted in new ways.

After our conversation on the surface, I couldn't help but see the marine life through a new lens. I marveled at how a thousand silver fish could somehow move in perfect unison. *It's the Influence Effect,* I thought. *They're all responding to those around them.*

I gazed around in wonder. *The power of groups is everywhere,* I thought. *Once you see it, it's everywhere.*

* * *

The dive ended all too quickly, and I bid a silent farewell to the undersea world as we returned to the boat. I struggled to climb the ladder with my heavy tank, and the crew more or less hauled me aboard like an enormous tuna. I turned to help Terry, but he was marching up the ladder like his tank was filled with helium. It seemed effortless. The guy was in unbelievable shape.

"That was amazing," I said, tugging off my mask.

Terry nodded, his face as serious as ever.

"Good work down there, Ethan. Excellent first dive. I could tell you hadn't forgotten your buddy."

"When a guy your size says I need to be accountable," I joked, "I'm going to pay attention."

Terry cocked his head as if he was considering something.

"Accountability isn't just about scuba diving," he said. "It's the main tool that we have as a Tribe to make things happen. One of the problems with being a leader, as most entrepreneurs and professionals are, is that there are fewer people holding you accountable each day. Sure, you have customers and investors. But they're not telling you what time to get up in the morning. They're not telling you which things to do when. And they're definitely not," he looked directly at me, "telling you to be on time."

I felt my cheeks flush.

"It's fine," he said. "But here's the lesson. You remember the Multiplier Effect from yesterday?"

"The right group compounds your efforts," I recited.

"Right. And you saw part of how that works. Clarity, creativity, connections—they all elevate what you're able to do on your own."

It was true. I'd seen it first-hand.

"But there's still a catch. For all the power of the Multiplier Effect, what a group can't do for you is take action. They can support, and advise, and even pitch in once in a while. But they can't do the work that needs to be done. Only *you* can do that."

I watched the sun scatter off the water into a million sparkles of individual light. "It sounds like you're saying that the group helps, but then—well, you're kind of on your own. Is that right?"

Terry looked out at the ocean. "If that were true," he said, his voice softening. "I'd be a very different person right now."

"How so?"

He continued to stare into the distance. I sensed he was trying to make a decision. At last, he spoke. "Would you believe I used to weigh almost two hundred pounds more than I do now?"

I felt my mouth fall open. "Actually, no. No, I wouldn't believe it. You're in incredible shape."

"I played a lot of sports as a young man," Terry said. "I was always big for my age. But once I started working—well, I got busy. The business, family, life. I started putting on weight, and not the good kind. I still had the appetite of an athlete, but none of the activity. I started gaining fast. Then I started eating even more. Stress, maybe? I still don't know, to be honest. But it was like the scale went up every day. Over the course of a decade, I gained almost twenty pounds a year."

THE THIRD EFFECT • 57

I did the quick math. "Whoa." That was all I could think to say. Terry gave a short bark that I thought was something like a laugh.

"Well said. Only I didn't have my *whoa* moment until I joined the Tribe. Suddenly, I was surrounded by all these healthy, successful, happy people. And there I was, hiding inside of two hundred pounds of fat."

He pulled his gaze back from the ocean.

"Not long after," he said, "I started exercising. Just walking at first. Then working out. Then running. Two years after I joined the Tribe, I ran my first marathon. When I crossed the finish line," Terry's voice became raspier, "I was a different person."

"Just from the Influence Effect?"

"That certainly started things off. At first, just being around the tribe changed how I saw things."

"And that was enough to turn you into a health fanatic?" I tried to keep the skepticism out of my voice, but I knew he heard it.

"No," Terry said, "that just made me realize how bad things really were. Even after that, I was still a couch potato. What really made the difference," he tapped the scuba tank at his feet with his toe, "was the buddy system."

"I'm not sure I follow," I said.

"Once the Influence Effect started to kick in, I saw things differently. I started to *want* to be healthier. I wanted to be like these new people I was spending time with. Then with the help of the Tribe—and the Multiplier Effect—I got some real clarity about where I was and where I wanted to go. The problem was, *I still had to do the hard work.* I had to eat better, and exercise regularly."

"Right—the group couldn't do it for you," I said.

"They couldn't. But what they *could* do," he said, "was make *me* want to."

At that moment the boat engines fired up, and we began to move through the sea, picking up speed as we headed for home. Terry began to methodically collect the gear into piles, and I helped as best I could.

"How did the group make you want to be healthy?"

Terry handed me my mask and fins and I stuffed them in the mesh bag.

"Your business is struggling," he said. "It may fail. Is that right?"

Ouch. "Yeah. I guess that about sums it up."

"Tell me this. Why do you care if it fails? Why do you keep showing up every day?"

"Because failing sucks."

"Not good enough. Why does it suck?"

"I don't understand. It just does."

"What if you were so wealthy that it didn't really matter?"

I thought about that. "I guess that would mean I could still pay the bills, but… no. It would still suck."

"Why?"

Damn this guy, I thought. *What a hardass.* "I think I would feel like I let everyone down. Jasmine has supported me through so much sacrifice. The people I'd hired would lose their jobs. That would be awful. My investors trusted me—I would have breached that trust."

Terry nodded gravely. "Right there. That's why. It's the buddy system. You feel *accountable* to the people who are important to you. To the people you've made commitments to. If it weren't for them, you could pack it in any time. But they keep you going—going through the pain, the struggle. The insurmountable problems."

He was right. I was motivated to succeed, certainly. But what was keeping me up at night wasn't really the business or the money. It was the people behind it all.

"Do you have any idea," Terry said, "how hard it is to exercise when you weigh 400 pounds? Trust me, it's hard. The only reason I crossed that marathon line is because this Tribe held me accountable.

My health was hitting crisis levels, and they helped me turn it around."

"They were like," I searched for the right word, "like dive buddies in life?"

Terry barked the gruff laugh again. "That's exactly right, actually. In the Tribe, we call it the Accountability Effect. It says that accountability is the world's most powerful force. While most of us are able to meet our basic responsibilities, few of us are held accountable to the things that matter most."

"So the Accountability Effect is the reason you started to make change?"

Terry looked out to the sea. We were closing in on the island, and I could see its volcanic peak looming over the jungle below.

"The Accountability Effect," he said gruffly, "is the reason I'm not already dead."

CHAPTER 7
ONE SHEET TO RULE THEM ALL

We helped the crew unload the equipment and rinsed it with fresh water. I bid a silent farewell to my octopus regulator, grateful I hadn't needed it, but still trying to process the lesson Terry had taught me.

"Thanks for the dive," I said to Terry, "and the insight."

Terry grunted what I thought was a 'you're welcome,' and continued to pack up equipment.

"And," I struggled to find the right words. "Congratulations on... well, changing. I'm glad you escaped the unhealthy Terry. I'm glad you... outran him."

Terry put down the wetsuit he was folding and looked at me strangely. He cocked his head again, like he was seeing something new.

Then he nodded curtly. "Thanks," he said.

And that was it.

As I walked down the pier, I pondered the Accountability Effect.

Accountability is the world's most powerful force, Terry had said. But what exactly did that mean? Clearly, it had worked for him—he'd gone from a walking heart attack to someone who was trim and healthy. But exactly how? I understood that he'd changed his lifestyle, but what was it about the tribe that made it happen? I still felt like I was missing a piece of the puzzle.

As I stepped off the dock onto the warm sand of the beach, I saw a familiar figure in the distance—the tall lean form of Simon in his distinctive hat.

I realized I'd seen very little of him since the first day. I waved, and he waved back, motioning for me to join him down the beach.

He smiled as I reached him at the water's edge. "How was your dive?" he asked, in his deep, clipped voice.

"The diving was great. The lesson even more so."

"Ah," Simon smiled, "the Accountability Effect."

"Did you know Terry when he joined the tribe?" I asked.

"Of course. And, to answer what you're not asking, yes, he was indeed in serious trouble. His health was very bad."

"He credits the Accountability Effect with saving his life," I said. "But I'm still not sure I understand how it works. I mean, Terry's transformation is remarkable. I don't think many people could have done the same thing in his position."

"Don't be so sure," Simon said. "Accountability can seem like a rare commodity, but we all have it. Do you remember on the plane when I told you that gathering in tribes was wired into us through evolution?"

"You said that natural selection led us to want to fit in with others. It was a survival advantage."

"Precisely. Accountability is an extension of that. Those who felt a responsibility and commitment to their tribe were an asset. They helped the tribe survive. And that meant that they reproduced more often. Therefore, those who were accountable passed their genes on. Thousands of generations later, we still have what you might call a legacy of accountability. We feel a sense of commitment to others. A need to keep our promises, follow through on our word. That can be an incredibly powerful force."

"That makes sense. But then why aren't we all more accountable?"

"Almost everyone experiences a sense of responsibility in some moments," Simon said, "but most of us are a little rusty. What we've done here in the Tribe of Millionaires is harness the power of account-ability in a way that allows people to tap into it on demand. We've taken something that's buried in your genetic code, and learned to activate it at any time."

I had to admit, that sounded impressive. Plus, I seemed to be surrounded by evidence every day that these principles worked. Every tribe member seemed... well, not perfect, of course. But accom-plished. Healthy. Happy. Like they were at the peak of their game.

Just like your father did, said a voice in my head.

I thought back to that day at the funeral home. How my father had looked *better* than when I'd last seen him.

"Of course," Simon said, "you shouldn't take my word for it. You should see it in action. Try it yourself. This evening we're going to put our system to work." He smiled warmly. "I'll see you for drinks on the veranda," he said, and turned to leave.

"Wait—before you go," I said. "At the funeral. I—" I trailed off. Simon waited while I fumbled to find the words.

"This might sound morbid," I said at last, "but I had this weird thought that my father looked better in a casket than he had twenty years earlier as a younger man."

Simon seemed to understand. "There are many things you don't know about your father," he said. "But, for now, let me say that I think you're probably right. A lot happened over those two decades." He motioned at the groups of Tribe members that dotted the beach. "Including all of this."

I thought back to the funeral. To Simon and the other men slip-ping the white cards under my father's clasped hands.

"The cards," I said, "the ones you and the others put in my father's casket—they're the same ones I've been receiving, right?"

Simon smiled. "Indeed. We all learned a lot from your father, but each of us—including you—has a lesson that we need most in life.

An effect that the right group can offer. Our job this week is to pass those lessons on. The cards are reminders of the things that are most important for those who want to lead meaningful, fulfilling lives."

"I understand the first two effects," I said. "But I don't quite see how the Accountability Effect plays out. One year Terry's on death's door, the next he's as healthy as a horse. How does the group help create that?"

"Ah," Simon said in his deep voice. "For that, we have a powerful tool. It's powered not only Terry's transformation, but many others. It's proprietary—only the Tribe has it—and extremely effective."

"Sounds impressive," I said. "I'd love to see it. What is it?"

"It is," Simon said, his eyes twinkling, "a sheet of paper."

And with that, he nodded, said goodbye, then turned and walked away.

* * *

Dinner that evening was on the main veranda—the same place I'd had my group brainstorming session the day before, and the place where the Tribe seemed to spend the vast majority of their time. When they weren't doing something active, they were on the veranda knocking around ideas, laughing—there was always plenty of laughter—or engrossed in quiet, intense conversation.

I arrived a little early and joined Simon and the other Tribe members for a drink. The room was buzzing with conversation, bursts of laughter, and even occasional shouts as the Tribe members ribbed each other good-naturedly.

I still had questions for Terry about the Accountability Effect, and I scanned the room for him, expecting to see his large form towering over a group somewhere on the veranda. When I did finally find him, I was surprised to see he was alone, tucked away in a corner. He was leaning over the table in front of him, deep in concentration. At times he would nod to himself. Moments later, he'd scribble something on the paper in front of him.

Simon followed my gaze. "You're going to see the Tribe at work again this evening," he said.

"What's he doing?" I asked.

"He's getting ready to engage the Tribe. To put the Accountability Effect to work."

I opened my mouth to speak, but Simon lifted a hand. "You'll see, Ethan. You'll see."

* * *

We sat for dinner, and after much jostling and pouring of wine and more of what I had come to think of as a sort of affectionate mayhem, someone clinked a glass, bringing the group to order.

I looked down the long table and saw Vikram, the chiropractor, holding a spoon and wine glass, calling the Tribe to order.

"Alright everyone," he said. "Let's get to this. Who's first?"

"I am." I recognized the gruff voice. I looked to the opposite end of the table where Terry stood with a single sheet of paper in his hand.

Vikram nodded at him and sat down.

"Okay," Terry began. "Let me give you my numbers first."

The last of the murmurs at the table died off.

Everyone looked to Terry, and he began to speak.

I was stunned.

Terry spoke matter-of-factly, as if he was reading something as ordinary as a shopping list. But what was coming from his mouth was anything but ordinary. In a few short minutes, he told the entire room the most intimate details of his life.

First, there was financial data—his income and his net worth, how much he gave to charity, and how much passive income he had. Then, there was physical data on his body fat, muscle mass, and exercise levels. Even some blood work. And he even had numbers for his personal life—how he rated his happiness and his relationship with his wife.

Halfway through Terry's recitation, I realized my mouth was hanging open. *This is crazy*, I thought.

For every number, Terry also revealed how much that number had changed over the previous year. After five minutes, I felt like I knew more about Terry than I knew about my best friends.

It's more than that, I thought. *You know more about him than you know about yourself.*

And that was just the start. When he finished his list of personal metrics, Terry began to talk about his plans for the coming year—plans for his business, for his family, for himself. I was particularly intrigued when he spoke of his health.

"So far this year," Terry said, "I have four marathons booked—one each quarter. That's an increase of two from last year, and I feel good about that."

A hand went up in the crowd. It was Davis—the short man with glasses who had offered the real estate advice during the brainstorming session.

"Terry," he said, "I know I speak for all of us when I say that your willpower is tremendous, and your transformation from when we first met is… well, it's remarkable. To see you up and running each morning while many of us are still sleeping—it's truly inspirational. You are a testament to exactly why this tribe exists."

There was a round of boisterous applause, and a few hoots and hollers.

"I know you've made great strides in many areas," Davis continued, "but I noticed that your life satisfaction has stayed the same, year on year. I'd like to ask you: what are you doing to change that?"

I saw Terry's jaw tighten. He took a breath, then visibly relaxed.

After a pause, he said, "As you all know, I took Ethan diving today. He was my buddy, and he handled himself well."

I looked up at the unexpected mention of my name.

"But he also taught me something."

Now I was truly surprised. What could I have taught *him?* I felt the heads at the table swivel my way. The room was silent.

"Ethan said something after our dive," Terry said. "He said he was glad I'd outrun the 'old Terry'. The unhealthy one."

I'd completely forgotten I'd even said it.

"That really hit me. I realized that…well, I *hadn't* actually outrun him. I was healthier, yes. I'd lost the weight. I feel good. But," Terry faltered, his voice cracking with emotion, "I'm still… I'm still running away from the old me."

There was a murmur of voices. A few people nodded at me.

It was Bruce who spoke first. "How can we help, mate?"

Terry took a deep, steadying breath. "I think you know I tend toward… well, let's say the somber side."

"Really? We hadn't noticed," cried a voice at the table.

There was a wave of laughter, and Terry cracked a small smile. I could see the relief wash over him.

"I don't think I'm exuberant by nature," he said. "I don't think anyone will ever call me jolly. But I think I have some bad habits. I work too much. And," he paused, as if considering, "perhaps I do work out too much, as well."

"What I'd like," he continued, "is for you to hold me accountable to doing something fun—not related to work or exercise. Just something enjoyable—at least once a month."

"No problem," Bruce said. "I'll check in… say, the first Tuesday of each month?"

"Perfect," Terry said. "Thank you."

I saw Bruce make a note in his phone.

Vikram spoke up. "Terry," he said. "I also find you tremendously inspirational. I'm certainly healthier because of your friendship, and I want to thank you."

Terry nodded.

"But I'd also like to push back a bit. You've signed up for more marathons this year."

Terry was silent.

"Do you think those extra races will make you much healthier?"

"Probably not," Terry admitted.

"And how do those extra races fit with your goal to stop running away from the old you?"

Terry's jaw clenched again. "They don't," he said, at last.

Vikram said gently, "Would you consider canceling one or two of them?"

After a pause, Terry said. "Done."

I saw Vikram make a note on the pad of paper in front of him.

* * *

Terry sat down to a round of applause. Moments later, our dinner arrived, and I realized I was ravenous. I tucked in like I hadn't eaten in a week.

After the main course, another member stood up to do his 'one-sheet', listing off his various numbers, revealing his goals, and asking for support in one way or another. After he sat down, another tribe member followed.

I began to see the pattern emerge. Every member shared not only what he was measuring, but how it had changed. Then they were able to ask for support and advice.

It was almost like the brainstorming session—I could see the clarity, creativity, and connection coming from the group—but there was an extra element. The person speaking was being held accountable.

The other members at the table seemed to have what I could only describe as a bullshit detector. If a Tribe member was avoiding something difficult or dodging what was important, they were called out on it—but in a very supportive and loving way. And then they were tasked with describing what they needed to get things done. Some members needed help getting to the gym. Others were blocked at making progress in their business, stymied by a certain next step that they, more often than not, were a little afraid of or confused by.

In each case, the Tribe rallied to support them and to promise to hold them accountable to specific actions.

* * *

There was a short break before dessert, and Simon took me aside.

"Well? Did that answer your question about putting the Accountability Effect to work?"

"And then some," I said. "I can see exactly how making things public and being held responsible to the group makes a huge difference."

"In fact," Simon said, "What's really happening is even more powerful. You're not being held accountable to the group. The group is there to make you more accountable to *yourself.*"

It was like a light went on in my head. *Of course. The group can't do the work for you.*

"Change is hard at first. But once you take action, it gets a little easier all the time. Eventually, Terry won't need the group to help him make time for some simple pleasures in his life. He'll be accountable to himself. The changes will be internalized."

"Like when he started exercising?"

"Exactly," Simon said. "Terry doesn't need our help anymore to get out for a run, or to eat better, or to go to the gym. He's become self-accountable for those things. But it's our job to hold him accountable in the areas where he hasn't yet developed that same capacity.

He'll turn to the group each time the challenge is greater, or the road more difficult."

"It's amazing. I think accountability might really be the world's most powerful force."

"In that case," Simon said, "How'd you like to go next?"

"What?" I felt my heart jump.

"You don't have to give as much detail as the others. Just ballpark your numbers, and then use the group to hold you accountable to something you truly want to accomplish."

My heart sped up even more. Could I really stand up there and talk about my business finances and my health? My income? My *marriage*?

"Well?" Simon said.

I took a deep breath.

"Maybe next time," I said.

Simon simply nodded. "Let's get dessert," he said. Then he patted my shoulder and walked back to the table.

I had the feeling he wasn't surprised.

THE THIRD EFFECT
SUMMARY

THE ACCOUNTABILITY EFFECT

Responsibility to others is the world's most powerful force.

- Most of us are not held accountable to the things that matters most.

- Accountability is wired into us by evolution—we just have to learn to activate it.

- The right group can't do the work for you, but they help by holding you accountable to yourself.

CHAPTER 8
THE FOURTH EFFECT

When the envelope slid under my door the next morning, I was already awake.

Part of it was expectation—I knew the envelope was coming, and I was anxious to learn what lay ahead.

The other reason I was awake, however, was that I wasn't entirely comfortable with how the previous evening had ended. When Simon had asked me if I wanted to really experience the Accountability Effect by doing my own 'one-sheet', I'd frozen like a deer in headlights. I'd refused, and while he hadn't pushed me, I had felt uneasy about my decision all evening.

Rather than take the initiative, I instead watched as another three tribe members stood up and delivered their one-sheet. Each time, I was first taken aback by the complete transparency of their presentation, and then blown away by the support of the tribe. With just a few questions and a handful of jotted notes, it seemed that they could transform a difficult challenge or a vague goal into a plan for action, backed by accountability.

It was so notable, so unusual, that I wasn't even sure how to describe it. I'd often seen successful people and wondered, "How do they do it?" Now, here on a tiny unnamed tropical island, I was being shown the answer. I was seeing right to the heart of what differentiated successful people from the rest of the world.

Yet, I'd turned down an opportunity to participate. *Why?*

That was what had awoken me early. I was here to make the most of the experience. I was here to *save my company*. Yet at the first glimmer of something difficult, I had cut and run like a scared kid. In the light of day, I was more than uneasy—I was *ashamed*.

My failure had kept me tossing and turning all night, and by the time the envelope slid under the door, I was on my feet to snatch it up almost before it slid to a stop.

I opened the door hoping to catch my mystery courier, but outside my hut, there was only sea breeze and morning sunshine. I was about to step back inside when I realized there was a small box on the porch. I picked it up and brought it inside.

I sat on the bed and opened the envelope. This time there were three pieces of paper inside.

The first was a white card, with yesterday's lesson:

THE ACCOUNTABILITY EFFECT

Accountability is the world's most powerful force.

I thought back to Terry, my dive buddy, and his remarkable transformation from obesity and poor health. From what I'd seen of him and the other tribe members in action, accountability really did seem like powerful stuff.

The envelope also held a folded sheet of letter-sized paper. Scrawled on the top was a short note:

In case you change your mind.

- S.

I unfolded the sheet to find a printed form. I scanned it and realized it was a blank copy of the single page the tribe members had been using the night before to deliver their one-sheet presentations. I looked it over briefly, noting the blanks to fill in everything from financial information to relationship details, health data, and goals.

Then I set it down. I was still deeply uncomfortable with the idea of sharing such personal information, but I wasn't quite sure why.

There was one more piece of paper in the envelope—another card, this one holding a note.

> *Good morning Ethan,*
>
> *Great day ahead today! If you can meet me at the main lodge for breakfast, I'll fill you in.*
>
> *Please bring the attached box—but don't open it yet!*
>
> *Best,*
>
> *Davis*
>
> *PS - Bring a beach towel!*

I scanned the blank one-sheet form again, still feeling vaguely uneasy about the whole thing, then I set it aside. *I'll deal with that later*, I thought. Besides, the day ahead felt good. Davis seemed much more cheerful than Terry, and anything that involved swimming suited me just fine.

I left the envelope and its contents on my dresser next to the other cards and notes. I tucked the small box in the pocket of my shorts so I wouldn't forget it, then grabbed a towel and headed out the door.

* * *

Davis was easy to pick from the group milling about the breakfast buffet. Where Terry was a looming giant with a serious disposition, Davis was his opposite in almost every way—a short, bespectacled, lovable nerd, he popped from group to group at breakfast, calling everyone 'pal' or 'buddy' or 'brother' and laughing endlessly at his own jokes. He was, I soon realized, impossible to dislike. He simply made everyone feel welcome. Like they belonged.

He approached me with arms open wide. "My software-making, habit-rewarding buddy," he said with a smile.

"I guess that's me," I said.

"You ready for today?"

I held up my beach towel.

"Good," he said. "One thing first. You were going to connect with me about the possibility of using your software in real estate."

Damn. I'd been so caught up in things, I'd forgotten.

"I'm sorry," I said. "I've been—well, I've been just trying to keep up."

His face grew somber and he peered at me. "Is that supposed to be an excuse?" he said.

I was taken aback by his serious tone. "No. I mean... I... I was—"

Davis grinned. "I'm just messing with you!" He slapped me on the back. "I heard that Terry busted your balls yesterday."

I let out a silent sigh of relief. "He did give me a good lesson on accountability."

"What he might not have told you is that accountability doesn't have to be intimidating. It's a powerful force, but it's not about *power*."

Davis led me to the buffet line, and we loaded our plates with fresh fruit as he chatted amiably.

"Imagine I'm your boss," he continued. "Because I have some power in our relationship, I can hold you accountable by flexing that power—using my status. You'll show up and do your job because otherwise, I can fire you."

"True."

"The catch is that accountability rooted in power is never the highest form."

"So what is?"

"That," Davis said with a grin, "is what today is all about."

We spent a few minutes in silence as we ate our breakfast, and

I pondered what Davis had said. I thought accountability worked much like the boss-employee situation he'd described. Yet, the more I thought about it, the more I realized it didn't really explain what was going on with the tribe. *There's something different happening here, I thought.*

I was about to ask Davis for more insight when I heard the roar of a small engine coming to life outside. Moments later, a second motor joined the chorus. Then another.

"That's our cue, buddy," Davis said with a grin. "Let's go!"

* * *

The noise grew louder as we stepped outside and descended the stairs into the clearing I had arrived at with Simon on my first day. *That seems like a year ago*, I thought.

The source of the noise was obvious. A long line of dirt bikes stood in the clearing in a semi-circle, their engines idling. I watched as tribe members loaded their towels and other gear into the back of a waiting jeep, then headed over to claim a bike and helmet.

I added my towel to the mix, but when I turned, all the bikes were taken.

A voice called over the roar of revving engines. "Ethan! Over here!"

I turned to see Davis grinning through the visor of a helmet. He was straddling one of the larger bikes.

"It'll be easier to ride with me your first time," he said.

I was dubious.

"Get on, pal. We've got ground to cover."

"Are you sure?" I said.

Davis pushed his visor up so I could hear him more clearly. "Ethan," he said, evenly. "Trust me."

I looked at the line of tribe members. They were all waiting on me.

I took a breath and climbed on.

* * *

For the first ten minutes I fought the urge to scream at Davis. To yell "*Stop!*" and jump from the bike and just walk away.

From where I sat behind him, I could barely see the road ahead. The roar of engines rang in my ears. A wall of green jungle flashed by me at what seemed to be increasingly insane speeds.

Are these guys crazy? Why didn't I get my own bike? I felt out of control. Corners arrived out of nowhere, and I had to grab Davis to keep from being tossed off the bike. Every rock or bump in the road seemed to lift me six inches off the seat without warning. The whole experience was terrifying.

Until… it wasn't.

Just as I had decided I'd be better off flinging myself from the bike into the jungle, I heard Davis's words in my head: *Trust me.*

My mind immediately flashed back to the night before. How I'd chickened out of doing my own one-sheet.

He's right, I thought. *I should trust him.*

If I was on this ride, then I was on it. I agreed to it. What good was it to freak out? It was clear Davis had done this many times. He was a skilled rider. What reason had he—or anyone here—given me to *not* trust?

I took a deep breath and I simply gave myself over to the experience. *Let's do this*, I thought.

And just like that, the ride went from terrifying to amazing.

* * *

Within moments, I forgot about whether or not I was going to die. As I relaxed, I realized that because I wasn't driving, I had the luxury of looking around. I watched the jungle flash by, seeing unusual birds, massive flowers, and towering trees—things I'd never seen before, anywhere. Even at this speed, the jungle was beautiful.

The more I relaxed and let go, the more I found the ride becoming somehow easier. I stopped fighting the bucking and turning of the bike, and began to move with it, leaning into turns, absorbing bumps with my legs. A few minutes later, I realized that I was grinning like an idiot.

I'm enjoying this, I thought. *Two minutes ago I was terrified, and now I'm like a kid on Christmas morning.*

Eventually, the landscape began to change. I started to see gaps in the impenetrable wall of green. Trees began to give way to rock. And then, just like that, we emerged from the jungle on to a broad expanse of black, volcanic rock, like a stone shelf set into the side of the island.

Davis stopped the bike. One by one, the remaining motors fell silent until the only sound was the faint ticking of the cooling engines.

A chugging sound grew from the silence, and I turned to see the jeep with our gear emerge from the jungle. It pulled to a stop beside us, and tribe members began shedding helmets and plucking towels and backpacks from the rear of the vehicle.

Davis tugged off his helmet and glanced at his watch. "We're a little early," he said. "We've got twenty-nine minutes to kill."

Twenty-nine minutes? That sounded absurdly specific. Was Davis more tightly wound than I thought?

I watched the other tribe members mill about. Some spread towels on the black rock, but most stood in the sunshine talking. It was clear we were waiting for something.

"What's going on?" I asked Davis.

"You'll see," he said brightly. "Did you bring the package I left for you?"

I reached into my pocket and handed the wrapped box to Davis.

"I understand you're feeling a little reluctant about the one-sheet," he said.

I felt my cheeks redden. "It's a lot to take in," I said. "I've never seen people be so—" I searched for the right word, "—so *forthright*. I think I feel a bit intimidated."

"Fear not," he said, and held up the package with a grin.

Davis pulled the paper off the small packet to reveal a deck of cards in a box. He pulled the crisp stack of cards from the packet, and I noted that each one was marked with the distinctive T o M logo.

"Let me make this easier for you," Davis said. "Did you ever collect baseball cards as a kid?"

"Sure."

"My childhood cards are long gone," Davis said. "Too bad—they'd probably be worth a fortune." He grinned. "But these," he held up the deck, "are a good substitute."

Davis spread out a large towel on the flat rock surface and we sat down in the sunshine.

"A baseball card has two sides," he began. "One side is the player's picture." He held a card with the T o M logo toward me. "The other side," he said, flipping the card over to reveal a jack of diamonds, "holds the player's stats.

"Think of the one-sheet like the back side of a baseball card," he said. "The side with the stats. Without that information, you don't really get a sense of a player. You're just running off what you see," he flipped the card over and tapped the T o M logo. "It's like trying to play poker using just the front side of a deck of cards. You're running blind."

Davis laid the jack of diamonds down on the towel, face up.

"Now here's where things get interesting." He pulled another card from the deck, with the logo toward me.

"Not only does the picture not tell you much, but it's also just a snapshot in time. It's static. Unchanging."

Davis flipped the card over and placed it next to the jack: the queen of diamonds. "But," he said, "as you get more information you get a clearer picture. Do that for long enough," Davis quickly flipped over another card next to the queen: the king of diamonds. "And you start to see a pattern develop."

Jack, Queen, King.

"In poker, that pattern tells you whether or not you're building towards a hand that's worth something. In baseball cards, you might see a baseball player building towards a World Series season."

Davis flipped over another card: the ace of diamonds.

"For *you*, the one-sheet tells you where you are, but also where you're *going*. Just like watching a player's batting average from season to season, or watching a poker hand build to a royal flush, the one-sheet lets you see the direction you're headed. And that's *really* important. The tiny things you do every day might seem small, but they stack up, and over time they chart the course of your life."

I stared at the line of cards. It made sense, but something was nagging at me.

"So the one-sheet helps you track your direction and progress," I said. "I get that. But couldn't I just track my progress, only… keep it private?"

"You could," Davis said, "and there would be *some* value in that. But let me tell you why it's important to share.

"In poker," he said. "You can't control what comes next. It's random. But in life, you can *change* the next card—like a ballplayer can change their next season. What drives that change is accountability. Whether the next card is an ace of diamonds," he flipped over an ace. "Or a not-so-good five of spades," he flipped over a five, "depends on accountability."

"How so?"

"There's a certain value in tracking things. In knowing your stats.

But what really makes the change happen is *sharing* the information. You can't be held accountable if you don't disclose the information to other people. That's like playing poker by yourself. The game's no fun without other players, and without some stakes."

I had to admit, that made a lot of sense.

"Plus," Davis said, "if you don't fully disclose, it becomes tempting to only reveal the good stuff to the world. Like social media—you become that person who only shares their best selfie, or the great hair day, or the vacation photos. Underneath all that you could really be struggling, but no one knows, because you're not sharing the whole picture. And that means no one can help."

I knew it was true. Yet, when I thought back to my embarrassment during the first group session—when the tribe had grilled me about my business—I felt a nervous churn in my stomach. Thinking about exposing all the details of my life and business didn't seem helpful. It just made me feel queasy.

I looked at the spread of cards before me—a nice line building toward a winning royal flush.

"I just feel strange about sharing all that information," I admitted. "How is it that everyone seems to do it so easily?"

"Ah," Davis said. He looked at his watch. "That's why we're here."

Davis swept up the cards and slipped them back into the box. "Just leave those here," he said, handing me the pack. "For what's next you won't need anything but your shorts."

With that, he stood up. "Okay guys, let's do this!"

* * *

Whatever was happening, it was cause for excitement. The tribe members stood up, and stripped off their t-shirts, and began to bunch together in a group. I looked at Davis, who nodded at me, so I followed suit. In moments, we all stood shirtless on the open volcanic rock.

"I'll bring up the rear with Ethan," Davis said. "Who's first?"
Terry raised his hand. "Got it," he said. He turned to the group.
"Guys. Remember to keep moving. No dallying. Get out of the way,
or get hurt. That's the rule."

Get out of the way or get hurt? I looked over at Davis, but he only
grinned and gave me a goofy thumbs-up.

Terry turned and began to walk toward the edge of the rock shelf.
The others began to follow.

I kept my eyes on Terry, trying to discern what was happening.
What was I supposed to do? What was I supposed to get out of the
way *of?*

Then, just like that, Terry *vanished.*

It was that sudden. One moment I could see his head, towering
over the nearest tribe members who stood behind him. Then his head
was gone.

I leaned, trying to see around the line of men in front of me, but
Terry had simply vanished. I stood on my tip toes. No Terry.

Then, as if by magic, another tribe member disappeared. The line
shuffled forward.

Then, in quick succession, two more vanished. There was no
sound. One moment they were there, the next they were simply *gone.*

From my vantage point, it was if their heads were simply disappearing. *What the hell was going on?* I felt my heartbeat ratchet up. I
turned back to Davis, but he simply grinned, clapped me on the back,
and nodded for me to keep moving.

I stood there, feeling increasingly nervous, the line inching forward. All I could see were heads vanishing. There was no sound. No...
anything.

I spun around to face Davis. "What the hell is going on?" I asked.

His face was now completely serious. "You wanted to know why
accountability works," he said. "You're about to find out."

I felt the knot of anxiety tighten in my stomach. I wasn't so sure I wanted to know anymore. I spun back toward the front of the line to see how many tribe members were left.

They were all gone.

And that's when I understood.

* * *

With the exception of Davis and I, everyone was gone. In front of me I could see a large, natural hole in the black rock shelf, perhaps three feet across.

I leaned forward and peered into the hole. Darkness.

Had they all climbed down here? I looked for ropes or some kind of ladder or even handholds, but there was nothing.

And that's when I realized they hadn't climbed. They'd *jumped*.

I turned back to Davis. "No way," I said.

"You're next, buddy," he said.

"You want me to jump in that hole? What's at the bottom?"

Davis said nothing.

I took a step closer, as close as I dared, and took another look. It was absolutely dark.

I turned back to Davis. He held up his wrist. "You've got thirty seconds," he said.

"Thirty seconds until *what?*" I said. Now I was feeling more than nervous. I was scared.

"Just do it, Ethan." The joking, amiable Davis had vanished. Now he was all business. "This is what you came for. You wanted to know how to succeed. How this works. What your father *created*." He held my gaze. "Well this is it. This is your chance."

"I can't."

"You don't get something for nothing, Ethan," he said, firmly. "These people? All this?" He waved his arm at the ocean, the bikes, the mountain, the *everything*. "None of this comes without risk. Without going further."

Davis took off his glasses and tucked them in the pocket of his shorts.

"You want to know the secret sauce? The magic ingredient? It starts here. It starts with me asking you this: *Do you trust me?*"

My brain was a swirl of thoughts. I felt my heart hammer in my chest.

"Ten seconds, Ethan."

Had my father done this? This...whatever it was? I thought back to the ride here—how I'd let go. Trusted.

Do you trust me?

I looked back at Davis. He said nothing. Just nodded, almost imperceptibly.

I turned. Took a breath.

And stepped into the blackness.

CHAPTER 9
THE GROTTO

I fell in absolute, terrifying darkness.

One moment I was standing in the sunshine, exposed on the hot, volcanic shelf; the next I was falling through utter blackness with no idea what was below.

Then, in an instant, it was over. I felt a painful slap on my feet, then I was engulfed in water. I quickly rose to the surface in the darkness, sputtering and heaving deep, panicky breaths.

The words flashed in my mind: *Get out of the way or get hurt.*

I began to blindly swim. I had just enough time to note the heads of the other tribe members floating in the dimness nearby before Davis rocketed into the water beside me and I was covered again in water.

I sputtered again, shaking off the salty water. A cheer erupted, echoing oddly. I stopped swimming and looked around.

My eyes had adjusted enough for me to see we were in a natural cavern—a sort of small, hollow volcano. Around me, tribe members bobbed in the water, high-fiving each other and chattering with excitement, their voices bouncing wildly off the walls.

I looked up. More than twenty feet above me, I saw a small circle of blue sky. *The hole,* I thought. The light from the opening illuminated the cavern enough for me to begin to make out the faces of the men around me.

We floated in place, treading water, and the chattering of conversation continued to grow, bouncing eerily about the cavern. Davis looked at his watch.

"Here we go," he yelled.

The voices lowered, then became murmurs, then stopped altogether.

I looked at Davis, not understanding. He just smiled. "Wait," he whispered.

And then it happened.

A hazy, wide beam of light shot almost straight down from the hole in the ceiling. It struck the water, transforming it. One moment I was treading water in an inky-black liquid, the next I was suspended in a green-blue sea so clear I felt like I might fall.

The light reflected from the ripples on the surfaces, bouncing wildly. The cavern walls, once black and almost invisible, were illuminated with a thousand flowing lines that danced unpredictably over the rough rock surface.

It was beautiful. The water was so clear it was like air.

I felt my mouth open in wonder. I leaned back, my legs rising in the salt water until I lay floating on my back.

I hung there, suspended in the crystal water. It was if I was floating in space, the cosmos spinning around me. In that moment, I forgot my troubles at work. I forgot the loss of my father. I forgot my uncertainty.

I became somehow aware that the men around me were doing the same thing, floating in silence, staring up in wonder. Sharing something that could only exist right there, right in that moment.

And then I forgot everything and we floated as one; soundless brothers in space and time, suspended in a kaleidoscope of light and stone and water.

* * *

We stayed that way for a few, long, magical moments, and then the sun continued on its path. The beam of light diminished. The water of the cavern grew dark and impenetrable.

No one spoke. In silence, we moved as one, following an unspoken command, and drifted from the cavern through a short tunnel, where we emerged moments later, squinting like newborns, feeling our way blindly into the light.

A set of stone steps had been roughly hewn into the side of the rock ledge. One by one, we climbed the rock face, streaming salt water, and lay on towels, drying ourselves in the sun.

There was no discussion, no debrief. There was no talking. Just shared silence as the sun baked the water on our skin leaving us bare to the world.

* * *

The ride back to the lodge followed the identical path as the one we used to reach the rock shelf, but it was anything but the same.

On the trip there I'd felt anxious. Even after I calmed down, I'd still felt—*something*. What was it? I struggled to name that feeling, then it came to me: I'd felt *separate*.

The plunge into the unknown had changed me. Now, I felt like I belonged. The drone of the engines faded away, and I watched as the bikes seemed to turn as one, leaning in unison, a single organism winding its way to a shared destination.

* * *

When we reached the lodge, the spell had begun to wear off. Some of the men headed for naps, others to the beach. I sought out Davis.

"That—today," I began, "it was—" I broke off, unable to express what I was feeling.

"I know," Davis said warmly. "We all know."

"You've done that before?"

"Every year. There's only one moment when the sun hits the rock at the right angle. Nothing like the first time, though."

We walked onto the large veranda and sat overlooking the sea.

"This might sound weird," I said, "but I felt different after. Changed."

Davis nodded. His joking demeanor had slipped away, again, shrugged off like a heavy jacket.

"You are," he said.

He was right, I knew. I could feel it. But *what*, exactly, had changed?

Davis seemed to read my mind.

"Do you remember when Terry mentioned you at dinner the other night?" he asked.

I thought back to the night when the men had presented their one-sheets.

"He said I'd made him realize that he might be running away from something," I said.

"Right. That wasn't just gratitude," Davis said.

"I don't understand."

"Earlier in the day, you'd gone diving. You were Terry's buddy," Davis said. He took off his glasses and polished them with his shirt. "That was more than just a tropical swim. Terry had to *trust* you. He had to know you had his back. During that dive, you earned his trust. That trust allowed him to be more comfortable. More open. More *authentic*. That's why he took what you said so seriously."

In the distance, I saw Simon and Vikram and a few other tribe members walking on the beach. "That's good to know," I said. "But how does that explain the feeling I had today?"

"I'm sure you know by now that the people around you matter more than you think," Davis said. "They change you."

"Right. They influence you. And multiply your efforts." I mentally ticked off the lessons in my mind. "And they hold you accountable."

"Precisely. But those around you aren't just a lens to help you navigate the world more effectively, they're also a *mirror*. They reflect you. They allow you to see *yourself* more clearly. And the closer the bond you have with those around you, the more accurate the reflection becomes."

"So I'm seeing myself more clearly because of today?"

"What happened today is that you learned to *trust*. And with that trust, you began to feel more comfortable being yourself. Your *real* self. Not some puffed-up version of you. Just *you*."

I thought back to the ride back. How I'd felt like I'd *belonged*.

"That's when the reflection is the clearest. When you're with people you trust. That's when you can let all the acting, all the insecurities, fall away. That's when you grow closer to your authentic self. And," he leaned toward me, "the closer you come to your authentic self, the easier life becomes."

"It does?"

"Absolutely. First of all, if you aren't sure who you are, it's difficult to know what you want. And if you don't know what you want, it's hard to get it." He smiled. "Once you feel comfortable in your own skin, you start to make better decisions. You might, for example, choose a better mate—one who truly fits you."

I thought about Jasmine. *That*, I thought, *is one decision I made right.*

"Or," he continued, "You might create a company or choose work that aligns with what you believe and who you are. And then you add friends and peers who complement that. Those are all things that are difficult to do when you don't know yourself.

"The best part," he continued, "is that authenticity helps you surround yourself with the right people. And the right people..." he trailed off.

"I know this one" I said. "The right people shape your destiny!"

"Exactly," Davis said. "All of that drives from trust. Yesterday, you saw how the Accountability Effect works. But what you didn't see is what allows it to work. The missing ingredient is *trust*. If you don't trust those around you, *none of this*," he waved his arm, "works worth a damn. There's no real influence. No multiplier. And definitely no accountability. You can't be held accountable if you aren't willing to be honest. To reveal your strengths and your weaknesses. Your dreams *and* your fears. You can't be held accountable to yourself if you don't know *who you are*."

I stare out the expanse of sea. "I still don't know if I know who I am," I said at last.

"That's not the point," Davis said. "The point is that the only way to find out is through people you trust. Until you trust others, deeply, and without prejudice, you'll never be yourself. You'll never know yourself. You'll never find yourself. Trust is at the core of authenticity."

I watched as Simon and the others walked up from the beach. They were smiling, chatting in easy conversation.

"This isn't just about your business, Ethan," Davis said. "It's about *life*. Your relationship with your wife. Your kids. Your parents. They're all improved by trust. Once you're willing to trust, you open the door to finding your true self.

"After that," he paused, smiling, "everything else is easy."

* * *

I spent the rest of the late afternoon and evening not just enjoying the surroundings, but feeling *wrapped* in them. Something had changed. I was no longer worried about what the tribe thought. I wasn't separate. I was, I realized, becoming a part of something.

It wasn't as if anyone had been judging me, I realized. The group hadn't changed. I had been judging myself. The only reason I hadn't felt this way from the beginning was the missing trust that Davis had spoken of. But that trust was building. The dive with Terry. The ride on the bikes. The terrifying, yet mind-expanding plunge into the grotto. It had all built my trust in the tribe.

And now? Now, I realized, I was feeling something new. I was feeling like…. like *myself.* My *true* self.

Through happy hour, and dinner, and early evening, I mingled easily. I felt happier, more relaxed than I had in weeks. No, *months.*

As the moon began to rise that night, I felt a new sensation. The comfort remained, but something else began to tug at me. It took a few minutes for me to realize what it was: unfinished business.

I made the rounds, said my goodnights, and headed back to my room. As I walked the torch-lit path, I felt my steps quicken.

I walked into my hut and went straight to my bedside table. The one-sheet form Simon had left for me sat folded where I'd left it.

I carried it to the small desk at the window. I sat, smoothed it out, and as the moon lit the beach and sparkled on the water, I began to write.

* * *

An hour later, I sat back. I was tired but pleased. The sheet had taken some work, but that wasn't the hard part. The hard part—building the trust—was behind me. I felt *comfortable. No,* I thought. *More than comfortable.* I realized I was *excited.*

I brushed my teeth and climbed into bed. *What an unbelievable day*, I thought. Another lesson learned.

As I closed my eyes, I thought of the elders of the Tribe. Simon, who I'd met first, and traveled here with. There was cheerful Vikram, with his bristly grey hair. Terry, the huge man of few words. Davis, the short, exuberant, funny man who'd taught me so much today. And I'd met Bruce already, although I hadn't spent much time with him.

My eyes flickered open.

There had been six men at my father's funeral. I'd met five of them. I had spent time with four of them.

Who was the missing sixth man?

I thought back to funeral, trying to pull the details from my memory. I vaguely recalled a lean rugged man. All the Elders were fit, clearly, but this man didn't look gym fit. He looked, well, *outdoors* fit. It was the only way I could describe it.

How old was he? I couldn't remember. And besides, with the tribe, I'd discovered it was hard to tell. But the picture in my mind was of a wiry man, grey, close-cropped hair. That was all I recalled.

But where was he? I hadn't seen him all week.

That was the last thought I had before I fell into a deep, dreamless sleep.

THE FOURTH EFFECT
SUMMARY

THE AUTHENTICITY EFFECT

You find your true self among those you trust.

- The people around you are a mirror that helps you see yourself more clearly.

- Trust is the key ingredient to find and align with your authentic self.

- The closer you get to your authentic self, the easier life becomes and the faster you achieve your goals.

Note: You can download the real-life tribal one-sheet!
You'll find the tool and helpful instructional videos at:
www.TribeOfMillionaires.com

CHAPTER 10
THE FIFTH EFFECT

I was dragged back to consciousness by an incessant pounding on the door. I stumbled out of bed, groggy and unsure. *What...? Where was...?*

It was only when I squinted around the room that I remembered where I was. *The island.* I thought of my plunge into grotto the previous day. *Had that really happened?*

There was another round of knocks on the door, followed by a muffled voice: "Mate? You up? Oy!"

There was no mistaking Bruce's Australian accent.

I stumbled out of bed, and opened the door, squinting as a blast of sunlight filled the room.

"G'day!"

Bruce, cheerful as ever, stood at the door holding an envelope. He wore a hat with one side of the brim turned up, Australian desert boots, and some sort of safari shirt with a seemingly unlimited supply of pockets.

I looked him over. "Really?"

Bruce looked down at his shirt. "What?"

"Never mind." I opened the door and motioned for him to enter. "I'm so sorry. I was dead asleep."

"No worries, mate. That trip to the grotto is always a bugger on your first go." He handed me the envelope. "Thought I'd just give you this myself."

I quickly ripped open the envelope, and removed the white card inside:

THE AUTHENTICITY EFFECT

You find your true self among those you trust.

"Good day yesterday, right?"

My head was starting to clear. "Amazing," I said. "And not just the grotto. The whole idea of trust and finding your authentic self."

Bruce seemed to consider something. "Right," he said. "On that whole trust thing, mate. I should tell you my name's not really Bruce."

I knew it. "It did seem a little," I groped for the right word, "much, I guess."

"It's a nickname. It's the Australian thing. My real name is Alan, but none of these bastards ever call me that."

"So… I should call you… Alan?"

"Nah, mate. Bruce is great," he said happily. "Just wanted to be straight with you."

I looked down at the card again. "Last night felt—well, different, somehow. I felt like I fit in. Like I belonged."

"Ah. That's trust at work."

"But it happened so fast. One minute I was the new guy, the next I felt like we were brothers in arms. It was that fast."

"That's the power of chemistry," Bruce said. "When you jumped down that hole, mate, your body was pumping neurochemicals like a firehose."

"Like adrenaline?"

"Oh yeah. And others—especially oxytocin. That's been called the trust molecule. It helps mothers give birth and nurse babies, but we all have it, and it's released during exciting times, and in social settings like meals. Even a hug releases oxytocin and increases trust."

Now that I thought about it, the tribe members were surprisingly physical, for me. There was a lot of hugging, slaps on backs, reassuring hands.

"So—I'm *bonded* to you all?"

"Yep. Think of brothers in arms, like you mentioned. They can be strangers, but a few intense experiences can bond them very tightly. I know veterans who have had four marriages—and counting, the nutters—but would still take a bullet for a guy they trenched with."

It made sense. Intense experiences did seem to bond people. And there was no question that I felt different after my adventure at the grotto.

"What's on for today?" I asked.

"Ah," Bruce said. "Today, we're going to do something really exciting."

* * *

Bruce left, and I quickly showered and dressed, promising to meet him at the main lodge.

As I brushed my teeth, I thought of his parting words—that we would 'do something really exciting.' I felt uneasy. I'd found my entire time on the island exciting, but occasionally terrifying—what the hell was something *really* exciting going to look like?

I thought of the previous day's message. *You find your true self among those you trust.*

I looked in the mirror. The face staring back at me was already turning brown from my few days in the sun. I looked different, at least on the outside. But had anything else changed?

You're going to have to let go and see where this takes you, I thought.

It didn't calm my nervous stomach, but moments later I stepped out of my hut and headed for the main lodge.

* * *

The tribe members were all gathered in the same clearing where we'd begun our trip to the grotto. This time there were no jeeps or motorbikes; if we were going somewhere, we were doing it on foot.

The group greeted me warmly, but I could tell something was different. The mood had shifted, and I sensed it had nothing to do with the previous day's sense of belonging. Something was up. No one was unhappy, but it was somehow more subdued. There was a sense of nervous anticipation.

I scanned the group, and spied the elders off to one side, deep in discussion. Simon, Vikram, Terry, Davis, and Bruce had been joined by a sixth man, and I recognized the look of lean, outdoor ruggedness about him. He was the missing sixth elder—the man who'd been at my father's funeral.

I couldn't hear what he was saying, but it was clear that the others were listening to him intently. He had an aura about him—a zen-like calm mixed with a natural leadership ability. He seemed quiet and contemplative, but somehow *durable*, like some strange combination of monk and cowboy.

I watched as he said a few more quiet words to the nodding elders, then I was interrupted as another tribe member tapped me on the shoulder in greeting.

By the time I looked back, the mysterious sixth man was gone.

* * *

We began to walk.

There was no instruction, no preamble. I had no idea where we were headed; I simply followed the group. After a few minutes, Bruce fell in beside me. I noticed he was the only member of the group who carried anything—a small backpack, stitched with, of course, an Australian flag.

I noticed we were following the same path I had taken days earlier with Vikram. I remembered he had taught me that the right people could multiply my efforts. *That seems like months ago*, I thought. I had been skeptical at the time, but now, just days later, I had no doubt it was true.

"Where are we headed?" I asked Bruce.

"Like, existentially?" Bruce smirked and walked on.

I shook my head. I was going to get no answers from him.

We continued on in silence, and I recognized the point where Vikram and I had turned back on our walk. We passed it and pushed on.

Uncharted territory, I thought.

It was all uncharted territory, I realized. The entire week had challenged what I believed about myself and the people around me. If someone had asked me a month ago if I thought I'd be spending a week on a remote tropical island with a group of mysterious millionaires with no idea *why*, I'd have said they were crazy. Now *I* was wondering if I was the crazy one. My life back home was starting to seem less and less sensible all the time. Why did I surround myself with the people I did? Why did my social and professional circle change so rarely? This whole week had challenged me tremendously. Why had it taken my father's death to shake me out of my life enough to get some perspective?

I wasn't sure I had any answers. All I knew was that my life back in the 'real' world seemed so... *unexamined*. I was just doing what everyone else was doing. I was spending all my time with the same people, doing the same things, believing the same things—without ever wondering *why*. When I contrasted that with my experience here, it seemed almost ridiculous.

The real world. The thought troubled me a little. Not just for the challenges I faced with my business—they were daunting, but I was beginning to at least see there was hope—but how would I settle back into *my* world? What would life be like when I was no longer hanging around with the mysterious Tribe of Millionaires?

* * *

The cool of the morning jungle was quickly giving way to the heat of the rising sun. The thick jungle offered some relief from the direct sun, but the humidity under the canopy was like a blanket. I was already sweating profusely, and as the trail turned uphill, I began to wish that I'd brought some water.

I looked around. None of the other tribe members seemed to be drinking. *Of course,* I thought, feeling edgy. *These guys are all too perfect to need to drink.*

To take my mind off of things, I turned to Bruce.

"Can I ask you something?"

"Of course, mate," he said amiably.

"All these things I've been learning," I said, "these effects that people have on us. They all make so much sense. And when I look at how successful you all are, it's so compelling. But..." I trailed off, trying to find the right words.

"But you're worried it'll all fall apart when you get back to the real world," Bruce said, his voice growing serious.

I looked at him. "How did you know?"

"Come on, mate. We're not superheroes. Look around you. We're all human. We all struggle with this stuff. We all have bad days. We all feel insecure at times. We worry."

"It sure doesn't look like it. Everyone seems... well, *amazing.* So successful, happy. Like you have it all figured it out."

"You need to understand something," Bruce said. "We don't come together like this because we're so amazing." He stopped walking and looked at me. "We're amazing because we come together."

"I guess that's the whole point," I said. "Being with the right people makes everything better."

"Exactly," Bruce said. "But you're right to consider what happens when you get home. It's one thing to keep your head on straight here. It's another thing entirely to do it when you get back to reality."

"So how do you manage it?"

"Well, for starters, we stay connected. We don't just do this once a year and then hope everything works out. Each of us belongs to smaller sub-groups, ideally ones that are close geographically. We talk every week. We help each other with challenges, with staying on track. And we get together as often as we can—not us, but we with our families and spouses, too. That keeps us in touch with what's important. It keeps us on purpose."

"On purpose—you mean accountability?"

"That's certainly part of it," Bruce said. "If I say I'm going to do something, the guys in my group will hold me to it. But purpose is something different."

"How so?"

"Let's say you set a goal to grow your business or improve your health. That goal is just a target. It's *what* you're trying to accomplish, or *where* you're trying to go—like a destination on a map. A purpose, on the other hand, is the reason you're trying to reach that goal. It's your *why.*"

"What does the *why* do?"

"The *why* is different from the *what.* The *what* is the destination, but your purpose is like the gas in the tank to move you forward. It's the drive, the energy, to keep going when things get hard. Because, believe me, at some point, things get hard."

They sure do. I felt a twinge of anxiety as I thought back to my impending cash shortages in the business.

"So," I said, "given a big enough *why,* you can accomplish more?"

"Given a big enough *why,* mate," the Aussie said, "and you can accomplish *anything*."

Then he strode off, leaving me with nothing but a dry mouth and more unanswered questions.

As the sun rose into the sky, we marched on.

The temperature began to soar.

* * *

The trail followed an uphill, gently curving arc. I suspected we were near the volcanic cone that dominated the island, but the jungle was so thick it was impossible to tell. Other than our narrow footpath, everything was a dense green wall.

As the sun rose higher, the heat and humidity climbed. With the damp air came mosquitoes. Plenty of mosquitoes. I noticed the other tribe members swatting at them.

To distract myself, I mulled over what Bruce had said—that with enough purpose, you could accomplish anything. Could it be true? It seemed like a tall order. But considering what I faced at home, a tall order was exactly what I needed.

I stepped up my pace to catch up to the cheerful Aussie.

"These mosquitoes are making me nuts," I said as I caught up to him.

"Mozzies? Never noticed," he said. I couldn't tell if he was joking, but I thought I saw a smirk cross his face.

"I've been thinking about what you said about purpose," I said, "What if I really want to be wealthy? Can't making money be my purpose? Then it would be aligned with my goal, which is to get my business into the black."

Bruce nodded, almost as if he were expecting the question. "I know that seems like a good idea," he said, "but if there's one thing I know for sure, it's that money makes a lousy purpose."

Something struck me. "If it's so important to find a purpose other than money, then why is this called the Tribe of Millionaires?"

I tried not to let the satisfaction sneak into my voice, but I knew there was a hint of *a-HA!*, as if I'd caught Bruce in the cookie jar.

"Ah, you're a sharp one, mate. Good question. For starters, it's bloody good marketing, right?" He gave a hearty laugh and slapped me on the back. "Got *you* here, didn't it?"

I had to admit, he was right. I flashed back to the moment in the elevator in Simon's office when I'd asked him what "T o M' meant. There was no doubt the money had been a turning point.

"Come on," Bruce said, as if sensing my embarrassment. "It's fine. Nothing wrong with it. As my mum used to say, it doesn't matter what door you come in, as long as you're home."

"I suppose. But it does make me question my motives."

"Mate, we all have a financial motive. Most of us spend the vast majority of our lives dealing with money—earning it, worrying about it, saving it, investing it. It's a big part of life. To deny it is simply foolish. The trick," he said, "is to understand that *wealth isn't a purpose.*"

"It just seems that we spend so much time focused on it. Like it's the biggest purpose of all."

"That's the trap right there," Bruce said. "We're all focused on the *how* of money. How do I earn it? How do I earn more? How do I invest it? How, how, how, how. What we should be focused on is the *why* of money."

I thought this over. "But seems like that it *is* why we all go to work. If we didn't make money, why would we do it?"

Bruce smiled. "That, mate, is exactly the question you need to answer. When you have that answer, you'll have found a purpose."

* * *

Bruce left me to ponder his words, and I settled back into the painful reality of the hike. I was dying for a drink of water, but as I looked around, no one else seemed to be drinking. Or complaining. So I trudged on, my tongue beginning to feel thick and pasty in my mouth. I could feel the fatigue in my legs, too. I wasn't entirely out of shape, but compared to the tribe, I was a full-on couch potato.

All this walking uphill was hard work. And for what? I wasn't even sure where we were headed, and Bruce seemed determined not to tell me. The relentlessly cheerful Aussie just trudged on. He didn't even seem to be sweating much.

I felt a blister begin to swell on my right foot. A seed of resentment began to form in my mind. *This is nuts,* I thought.

* * *

My thirst began to intensify.

Before long, I was thinking of nothing but water. *Anything for a drink.*

As if in answer, there was a crash of thunder, and a heavy rain began to fall. Within seconds, any part of me that wasn't already soaked in sweat was drenched in rain.

Unbelievable. Of course, it would rain.

I realized the other tribe members were staring up into the sky, catching the rain in their mouths, and I did the same. I stood, gaping upward, letting the rain fall into my open mouth. Even in the heavy downpour, it wasn't much, but it was something. I swallowed the little water that I managed to catch, then opened my mouth again for more. I stared into the canopy, squinting into the pouring rain, catching what moisture I could.

When at last I lowered my gaze, the path ahead was empty.

The tribe was gone.

* * *

My first feeling was one of anxiety. *I'm alone.* Then I realized that the trail was obvious, and there had been no forks so far—finding the tribe shouldn't be hard. I broke into a brisk walk, expecting to find them just around the corner, but at the next bend, I saw no one.

I pushed on in the rain, now jogging along the path, and my anxiety began to be replaced by the growing irritation I'd felt earlier. *Why had they left me?*

My shoes were soaked, and I felt my blisters grow. The rain had muddied the path, and as I rounded a bend I slipped, falling hard.

"Damn!" One side of me was completely covered in mud. I'd twisted my ankle, too. I could still walk, but it wasn't improving my state of mind.

I stood, flexed my ankle carefully, then pushed on. Minutes later I still hadn't seen anything but footprints. *How fast were they moving? Had they left me on purpose?* Questions, then doubts, began to enter my mind, and through it all came a growing sense of futility. *Where the hell were we even going, anyway?* My mood worsened.

As I trudged on, the rain tapered off, and the sun reemerged. Even through the forest canopy, I could feel the intensity. The temperature began to climb further.

Abruptly, the jungle gave way to heat and open space. One moment I was in the shaded green of the jungle, the next I was standing on bare rock in the open air and blazing sun.

I realized I'd finally climbed high enough to rise above the treeline. Now, I stood on the black volcanic rock of the mountain itself. In the distance, I could see the ocean, and far, far below, the beach that fronted the main lodge.

The trail, which had been a dirt path, was now a hewn rock ledge. To one side was a sheer drop facing the sea. To the other, a steeply sloping wall of stone. My eyes followed its slope upward, and high above me, I could just make out the conical peak of the dormant volcano.

Closer—perhaps a hundred feet or more above—I saw what looked like another path cut into the stone, just like the one I was one. I looked back at the path I was on. The wide stone ledge curved gently upwards, and around the volcano, eventually disappearing from view.

I looked back up at the path above.

Then it hit me.

We were going to the top.

And not only were we going to the top, but we were almost certainly taking this slow, spiraling path that circled the volcano over and over.

How far was it? I looked to the peak and tried to judge, but I had no idea beyond a certainty that it was hours and hours of walking on hard stone rock, exposed to the blazing sun, with no food or water.

I stared back up at the distant peak, squinting into the burning light. The heat was like a blast furnace. The sun beat down relentlessly, soaked up by the black rock of the mountain, and forced back out at me like a hot stagnant breath.

Beneath my feet, the heat of the rock seeped through the soles of my shoes. My feet had begun to swell; I could feel each blister like a hot coal. My thirst raged.

There's no way, I thought. *I can't do it.*

I put my back against the rock and looked out at the ocean. I leaned my head back into the sliver of shade and slowly slid down until I sat, sunburned, dehydrated, and dejected, on the black stone of the mountain.

CHAPTER 11
THE CLIMB

The leg cramps woke me.

Both hamstrings had seized, clamping me in a grip painful enough that I cried out. I gripped the backs of my thighs, gritting my teeth against the pain, and began to massage the seized muscles.

When the ache had subsided enough for me to focus on something more than the pain, I noticed that my thin sliver of shade had expanded; the sun had moved, and I was now almost completely sheltered.

How long have I been asleep? I tried to get to my feet, but the cramps grabbed my thighs again in vice-like grip. At the same moment, bolts of pain shot through my feet as my shoes squeezed my blisters.

I fell back against the stone.

I can't.

I can't go any further.

In that moment, I made my decision: it was time to go home. Not just back to the lodge. Not just back to food and water. But *home.* Back to my real life. It was time for the experiment to end. I had a company to save. I had a family to care for.

I began once again to massage my aching hamstrings. I would crawl if I had to, but I was going back. I'd had enough. I knew there was no possible way I could climb any higher. What little strength I had left I would use to get back to safety, and then back to reality.

It was, I told myself, the only sensible choice. After all, why push on? I had nothing to prove out here. Nothing to accomplish. Whatever lesson Bruce was trying to teach me, he could teach me back at the lodge over dinner and cold drinks. Plenty of cold drinks. And then I'd grab the first flight out of here.

I gave my reluctant hamstrings one more rub and using the stone wall for support, I carefully stood. It was painful, but I was at least upright. *And going back will surely be easier*, I thought.

I turned to begin the trek downhill.

That was when I saw the backpack.

It was small, carefully placed in the very center of the trail home, its straps neatly folded beneath it. There was no way I could miss it. And there was no mistaking who it belonged to; sewn to the top pocket was an Australian flag.

Bruce, I thought. I sat beside it and unzipped the top.

Inside the pack was a rectangular wooden container, no bigger than a shoebox. And beneath it, a bottle of water.

I barely registered the box, but stripped the lid off the water bottle and drank deeply. It was the best thing I'd ever tasted, and I gulped at the water until the more rational part of me said, *easy, Ethan. Easy.*

I felt immediately better. The last of the tightness in my legs subsided. I carefully screwed the lid back on the bottle, then turned my attention to the box. *Maybe there's food*, I thought.

The box was ornate and beautifully crafted, made from a wood I didn't recognize. Its sides were so well polished that they seemed to glow from within. On the lid, the letters T o M had been carefully carved.

There was a small brass catch. I unclasped it and lifted the lid. A white tribal envelope lay inside, and I opened it to find a white card.

THE PURPOSE EFFECT

The right people reveal your richest source of power.

I thought back to what Bruce had said. About *why*. Was that what he was trying to tell me? That I needed a powerful reason? But for what? My big *why* right now was to get something to eat and drink, and to put my feet up on something soft.

I set the card aside and turned my attention to the box. A carefully wrapped black cloth bundle lay inside, embroidered with the tribal logo. It was soft and gave way to my touch.

There was a small brass plate affixed to the underside of the lid. Engraved on in a fine, sloping script were the words:

Roberto Martinez

Beneath the name were two dates. I recognized them as the years of my father's birth and death.

I looked again at the carefully wrapped package.

And then I knew.

* * *

I don't know how long I stared at the cloth bundle in the box. When I looked up, I realized I was still facing downhill, back toward the lodge. *Back to safety*, I thought.

And back to being alone, a different voice seemed to say.

Behind me, upward, lay the unknown. A hard march. A lot of pain. Perhaps danger. But in that direction, I realized, there was now something else: a *purpose*.

For all my misgivings about my father, for all his failures, I was here right now because of *him*. Everything I'd learned this week, the sense of belonging I'd discovered, and the lessons I hoped could save me and my company—they had all, whether I liked it or not, been handed to me by my father. Placed in my hands by a man I barely knew.

I looked down at the ornate box.

And in return, you're being asked to do one thing, I thought.

I gently closed the lid and returned the box to the pack. I took a small sip from the water bottle, then carefully capped it and stored it away.

The white card I stuck in my pocket. It would probably be soaked in sweat and grime, but I didn't care. I knew I would need it close at hand.

I tested my feet: sore, but I could walk. I *would* walk.

Then, I shouldered the small pack holding my father's ashes, and began to make my way slowly uphill in the direction of the tribe.

* * *

It was slow going at first. My feet ached. At some point, I felt the blisters swell, then pop. But I pushed on.

My lips cracked in the sun, and I was thirsty. Very thirsty. But somehow, I knew I could manage. I took occasional, careful sips from my remaining water, and simply pushed on.

The thought of stopping no longer entered my mind. At times my negativity would start to build—I'd notice the fatigue in my legs, the pain of my sunburn, the cracking of my lips. My steps would falter. But in those moments, I reached into my pocket for the white card and reread the Purpose Effect. I thought often of Bruce's words: *With the right purpose, you can accomplish anything.*

Then, I would think of my friends somewhere up ahead—at some point, I realized, I'd stopped thinking of them as tribe members, and began to see them simply, powerfully, as friends—and I'd think of my father's ashes, nestled carefully against my back.

My resolve would build, then, and I would walk on.

Now that I had a purpose—and the right people to remind me— my fatigue had faded into the background. The suffering wasn't gone; I was in constant pain, and at some level I was aware that my steps had shortened, and I was perhaps closer to stumbling than walking. But it was as if my doubt had been replaced by something more important.

Purpose, I thought.

And I pushed on.

* * *

I had been right about the path. The mountain was far too steep to climb directly, and so the trail simply wound its way around, slowly gaining altitude.

Who built this? I thought at one point. Then the thought vanished as another wave of fatigue washed over me. I thought of my friends. And my father. And I trudged ahead.

As the sun moved lower in the sky, I began to find more and more shade on one side of the mountain, and I instinctively sped up during those cooler, protected sections.

When I rounded to the sunny side and entered the blast furnace of the afternoon sun, I slowed, sometimes taking the now-battered card from my pocket, and holding it in front of me, like a compass.

And I then I would push on.

* * *

The path seemed to spiral forever. I trudged forward, stopping occasionally to take a tiny sip of water. At some point, I lost my voice, and when I spoke to myself it was in a hoarse, painful whisper.

As the sun fell lower in the sky, the shady side of the mountain grew cooler, but the sunny side seemed to only grow hotter, the black rock of the mountain too hot to even touch.

In those moments I simply stumbled forward, my eyes squinted against the glare, my tongue swollen in my mouth, and prayed for an end to the heat. When I thought I could go no further, I would feel the reassuring weight of the box against my back, and I would put another foot down, and take another step.

It was in this way, step by painful step, driven forward by the sole purpose of carrying my father to his resting place, that I found the tribe.

* * *

Dusk had fallen on the mountain. With it came enormous relief from the heat, but a new fear: *what would happen after dark?* I wasn't sure I could safely find my way forward, but I was equally uneasy about spending the night perched just a few feet from a plunge to my death.

I was trying to focus, to consider my options, when I heard a sound. *Voices.*

I pushed forward toward the noise. When I rounded the next corner, I saw a flicker of orange light ahead and heard the sound of conversation.

I moved closer, my legs deadened, my feet screaming, and as I emerged into a clearing, I found the men seated around a large campfire.

The conversation trailed off as I teetered unsteadily into the center of the light.

So thirsty.

I scanned the faces in the circle until I spotted Bruce.

He stood, tentative. Uncertain.

I stared at him. There was a very long, very silent moment.

"G'day, mate," I whispered.

He broke into a broad grin, stepped forward, and embraced me in an enormous bear hug.

The men erupted in cheers. Hands slapped me on the back.

Someone put a cold beer in my hand. *A cold beer.*

I lifted it to my lips and drained it.

That's the best thing I have ever tasted, I thought.

Then everything went black.

* * *

"Mate? You good?"

I opened my eyes to find Bruce staring down at me.

"Jesus," he said, relief flooding his face. "You scared the bloody hell out of me."

I could feel the rock ground against my back, and I struggled to sit upright.

"Lucky I was here to catch you," Bruce said.

I rubbed my eyes and looked around. The tribe members were all staring at me.

"I think I might have pushed it a bit too—" I broke off as I remembered the wooden box. "The backpack!" I said, scrambling to my feet.

"Right here, mate. Right here." Bruce handed me the pack. "Easy does it."

Someone placed a bottle of water in my hand, and I took several long swallows.

"I'm not sure how I made it this far."

"I think I have an idea," Bruce said, nodding at the backpack.

I looked down to see I had the bag clutched to my chest in a white-knuckle grip. I relaxed and lowered it, then reached into my front pocket and pulled out a barely-recognizable white T o M card. It was soaked in sweat, stained and battered, but the print was still legible.

"This helped," I said, showing Bruce the card.

"With the right purpose—" Bruce said.

"You can accomplish anything," I finished.

* * *

A few bottles of water and a good meal later, I was feeling

remarkably restored.

From what I could tell in the dark, the fire I had nearly fallen into stood at the center of a flat, open area on the side of the mountain. The tribe had set up camp on this plateau; how they'd done it, I had no idea, but after my experience that day, I was beginning to see that *how* something was done was far less important than the reason *why*. Clearly, this ritual was important to the tribe.

We sat around the fire, cross-legged. My blistered feet still ached, and I could tell my face was badly sunburned. Still, I felt strangely satisfied, almost peaceful.

"I don't know how I made it," I said to Bruce. "I was going to quit," I confessed, "and then I saw the pack."

Bruce shrugged, as if it were obvious. "That's the power of purpose," he said.

I looked around at the tribe members, engaged in smaller groups, deep in conversation. "Every lesson I've learned here," I said, "is about how the people around you can impact your life. This idea of *purpose*—how does it fit? Purpose seems very individual."

Bruce stirred the coals of the fire.

"You're right," Bruce said, "everyone's *why* is unique and personal. The challenge with *why* is that it's easily consumed by *how*. We get caught up in the day-to-day. It's easy to lose sight of your purpose or to have it hijacked by things like money, or power, or beauty. Those things don't endure, yet they have a way of leading us away from purpose."

"And the tribe?"

"The tribe brings you back," he said, poking the embers of the fire. "The right people reveal your richest source of power. They keep you on purpose when you can't do it yourself."

* * *

A delicious meal behind me, I felt much restored. But I was relieved to see that although they were nowhere as exhausted, the tribe members all seemed ready for an early night.

Our camp was a series of simple canvas tarps strung over ropes. The simplest of shelters, with the barest of bedding on the hard rock.

But for all its rugged simplicity, I lay down, took one look at the stars through the open end of my tent, and fell into a deep and dreamless sleep.

THE FIFTH EFFECT

SUMMARY

THE PURPOSE EFFECT

The right people reveal your richest source of power.

- Wealth is only a tool—it's a means, not an end.

- A powerful purpose can help you overcome the greatest obstacles.

- Surrounding yourself with the right people keeps you in touch with your *why*.

CHAPTER 12
THE SIXTH EFFECT

My eyes flickered open.

The thought came instantly: *This is my last day.*

I lay on my back, staring at the ropes and canvas tarp that served as my tent. I gingerly flexed my feet. They were sore, but I'd be able to walk. A few bandages and a good sleep had served me well.

It was hard to believe how much had happened in a week. My father's funeral, and meeting Simon. Traveling to this island and meeting the Tribe of Millionaires. The diving, the grotto, the adventures. The quest to carry my father's ashes up the side of an ancient volcano. It was a week that seemed to last both an instant and a lifetime.

Despite the fact that I was camped on the peak of a tropical mountain, I began to feel the tug of home. Not just the pull of the familiar—of my own bed, of my routine, of Jasmine—but a growing sense of uncertainty, too. A week had passed here, but it had also passed at home. My company was still deeply troubled. There was work to be done, there was a team to be led. There were problems to be solved.

My mind began to churn with the thought of what was waiting for me.

Had I learned enough? I thought of Simon and the other elders, and the lessons they'd taught me. There was no question I'd learned a lot, but was it enough to save my company?

I mentally reviewed the lessons of the week. *Influence. Multiplier.*

Accountability. Authenticity. Purpose. I knew they were powerful, but could I apply them?

That was a problem I'd solve at home. For now, I had one day left, and one lesson to learn.

Gingerly, I sat up in my sleeping bag and peered out at the breaking dawn. From this height it was breathtaking. I unzipped my sleeping bag, to go closer to the edge of the mountain for a full view. At my feet, laying crisp and white against the black stone of the mountain, was an envelope. Inside, an embossed card carried the lesson of the previous day—reprinted on fresh paper.

THE PURPOSE EFFECT

The right people reveal your richest source of power.

I thought back again to the previous day's struggles. Just twenty-four hours ago, I would have dismissed the card as a nice platitude, nothing more. In light of what I'd accomplished, it now seemed like I'd been handed the world's most priceless wisdom.

I reached into my pants pocket. I had, not surprisingly, fallen asleep in my clothes. I pulled out the torn and battered version of the same card and recalled how much it had meant the day before.

At the darkest moment of my climb, when I was burned and thirsty and broken, I had given up. I honestly believed I couldn't go any further. Then, when Bruce helped me find a powerful *why*, I had found the strength not just to push on a little further, but to push on for *hours*. It was the hardest thing I'd ever done. And also the most rewarding.

I reached for the wooden box holding my father's ashes. I had slept beside it, and now I placed both cards in the box next to the carefully wrapped bundle.

I looked inside the envelope for a note to tell me what to do next, but it was empty. I felt a momentary rush of anxiety. *Was it over?* I was so certain there'd be another lesson, something to tie it all together. But was that just my assumption? Had Simon or anyone else ever actually said how many lessons I'd learn?

What do I do now? I thought. *Was this it?*

My spinning mind was interrupted by a sound.

I looked up to see a man squatting on his haunches at the opening to my tent. *Where had he come from?*

The tanned, rugged face. The stubbled, shaved head. The piercing eyes. That aura not of authority, but of steady competence. It was the missing elder—the mysterious sixth man that I had seen at my father's funeral.

"Good morning, Ethan." He had a deep, warm voice, the slightest southern hint. Soft, but powerful. "My name is Mason," he said, extending a calloused hand. "I was your father's best friend."

* * *

With that barest of introductions, the mysterious elder stood and walked slowly away from the camp. I stepped out of the tent to follow, then paused, indecisive. I ducked back under the canvas and picked up the wooden box, then limped slowly in the direction Mason had taken.

The small plateau where we had made camp ended in an abrupt drop, where the view widened to a complete panorama. I stopped, captivated. The breaking dawn was spreading an orange glow across the sea. We were thousands of feet up. *No wonder my feet are sore*, I thought.

I looked around for Mason and spied a trail leading off from the plateau. Skirting the edge of the cliff, I followed the path, which quickly turned into a steep uphill climb.

Here we go again, I thought. But the climb was short, and moments later I found Mason perched cross-legged on a narrow ledge, watching the sunrise. I inched my way nervously closer, the box clutched to my chest. In front of me was a nearly sheer drop of thousands of feet.

As I reached Mason, I discovered to my relief that the ledge widened considerably, and I could sit quite easily with no fear of falling. I realized we were at what must be the highest point of the mountain. The ocean stretched out in every direction, sparkling in the morning sun.

"I see you brought someone with you," Mason said.

I looked down at the box but said nothing.

"The last time I was here was a year ago," he said, "and I was with your father." He stared out at the ocean, but I could tell he was looking at something that was no longer here.

"He was sick, then," he said. "He didn't say anything, but I think he knew. We sat here for a long time, just like this. And he talked and talked." A smile played at his mouth. "I'd never heard your father talk so much."

"I guess I wouldn't really know," I said.

Mason nodded as if considering his next words.

"Yesterday," he said, "how did you feel when you found yourself alone?"

I thought back to my near-breakdown on the trail. "Angry, at first. I was tired, thirsty. To be honest, I had decided to give up."

"What changed your mind?"

I looked down at the box, still clutched in my hands. "This," I said.

"So," Mason said, that slight smile playing around the corner of his mouth again, "it helped to have some extra weight to carry?"

"Very funny," I said. But he did have a point. How did carrying more make climbing the mountain *easier*? "I know it was the Purpose Effect that made the difference," I said. "I'm just not sure I understand *how*."

"One of the great secrets of life," he said, "is that we are all capable of far more than we imagine. Your father was fascinated by this idea—it became his lifelong quest to find out how to tap into that vast store of potential."

"Where did he get the idea?" For me, this was yet another unknown aspect of his life.

Mason turned his attention from the sea to the ground beside him and picked up a jagged piece of volcanic rock.

"Way back in the 1930s," he began, "long before your father was born, a man named Kurt Lewin wrote an equation. Your father mentioned it often. He used to tell me that Lewin should have been as famous as Einstein and that his equation should be as well-known as $E=mc2$."

Mason used the rock to scratch some characters on the stone ledge, where they stood stark white against the dark rock:

$$B=F(P,E)$$

I stared at the letters. "That's Greek to me."

Mason tilted his head, examining the writing. "It's not as complicated as it looks. What it says is that someone's *behavior*," he motioned to each letter in turn as he spoke, "is a function of the *person* in their *environment*." He scratched a line under the equation. "In essence," he said, "people act differently depending on their surroundings."

"I guess that makes sense," I said.

"It does, yet most people go through life believing something quite different. They are convinced that how they think and behave is due to their personality, or some other inner state. They don't realize that, below the level of their consciousness, the world around them is constantly influencing their behavior."

"That sounds like the Influence Effect."

Mason smiled, a full grin this time, and it lit his rugged face.

"Like father, like son," he said. "Roberto loved the idea of influence. But he was fascinated by how one part of the environment, the *people*, affected behavior. He didn't care if northern latitudes made you depressed, or if growing up poor made you anxious. What he cared about was how the people in your life changed you. The Influence Effect was your father's first effort to try to codify what he was learning about how people impact our destiny."

"So he started the tribe?"

Mason chuckled. "What you see now is a far cry from where things started, but, yes. He wanted to move beyond just knowing that people change us. He wanted to consciously *harness* those effects. It's one thing to understand that the people around you have an effect. It's another thing altogether to build a system that can use that knowledge. The tribe is that system."

I thought of how accomplished all the tribe members seemed.

"It's hard to deny that it works," I said. "Everyone here is so—" I struggled for the right words, "so *successful.*"

Mason made a non-committal grunt.

"I mean," I continued, "I've never seen so much money, so much accomplishment in one place at the same time."

"It's no secret that we all appreciate the benefits of wealth," Mason said. "We don't call it the Tribe of Millionaires because we're broke."

"Bruce told me yesterday that wealth couldn't really be my purpose."

"Well," Mason said. "It *can.* It's just not a very satisfying one. Do you remember the Multiplier Effect?"

"That the right group of people compounds your efforts?"

"Exactly. Money is like that—it's another multiplier. But what it multiplies is up to you. You can use wealth to gain power or to consume more and more. You can use it to keep score, or to boost your ego."

"Or," he stood, and tossed the rock from the cliff edge. I watched it sail out, and then drop from sight. "You can use wealth as a tool to enable you to fill a higher purpose."

"Is that what Bruce meant? About purpose?" I asked.

Mason sat down beside me again. "Life will give you whatever you decide to demand of it," he said. "I hope you've learned by now that, with the right people around you, you can accomplish anything. The point is that you need a *reason* to demand things—a purpose—and the reason can't be the things themselves. Bruce's role is to show how the tribe can help you find and follow your unique purpose through different stages of life."

"Then what's your job?"

"My job is different. It's to make sure we connect to the one purpose we all share."

I thought of the tribe. Of Simon's fancy office. Of this beautiful private island.

"The only thing I know for sure you all share is wealth," I said. "Everyone is so different."

Mason nodded thoughtfully. "You know the old saying," he said, "that 'no one ever dies wishing they spent more time at the office'? I believe—and your father did, too—that deep down we all know that work isn't everything and that you can't take your wealth with you. What's difficult is for us to keep that in perspective."

"So how do you do it?"

Mason smiled at me. "You've been here for long enough. Why don't you tell me?"

"Let me guess," I grinned. "By surrounding yourself with the right people."

"Exactly," Mason said. "The tribe teaches us to better ourselves. To master our health, our wealth, our relationships. But more than anything, the tribe keeps connected to the one purpose we all share."

"Which is what?"

Mason seemed to ponder this. "Do you remember the one-sheets?" he asked.

With a flush of embarrassment, I thought about how I'd been too intimidated to participate. "Yeah. I do."

"The one-sheet is a scorecard. But at the end of life, there's only one score that's going to matter. You might call it the ultimate one-sheet. You only get to fill it out once, and all the math happens in an instant—that instant when your life flashes before your eyes. It's that moment when you face the end of your life, and you look back and wonder, "Why was I here? What did it all *mean?*"

"That sounds like a question that has no answer."

"It does sound that way. And there was a time when I certainly believed that. So did your father—in fact, for years there were only five effects. The sixth was added in his final months of life. When he knew the end was near. When everything was being stripped away—literally and figuratively—and he was left with the simple knowledge of what matters most. That's what he shared with me on our last trip here."

We sat in silence. I imagined my father and Mason sitting just like this, watching the sun.

"What did he tell you?"

"Your father was an imperfect man, Ethan," Mason said. "And there's no shame in that. None of us is perfect. But he tried. He deeply regretted his early life. He deeply regretted that he couldn't reach you—that he'd lost you. Of all the lessons he left for us, this one more than any other is the greatest. It applies to everyone. But it was written for *you.*"

Mason held up his hand. He had a white envelope pinched between his fingers. I opened it and read the card inside.

THE CONNECTION EFFECT

*Your life will be measured by
the quality of your relationships*

A flood of images poured through my mind. Of friends. Of family. Of Jasmine. Of all the important moments in my life, and how they all involved other people.

"There's a tide in life," Mason said. "It's not strong. It's not a tidal wave. It's a slow, invisible, inexorable force, and year by year it pulls us from each other. Your job in life—the one that matters more than any other—is to hold on to those around you. To make sure the tide doesn't pull you from the people that matter most."

I stared at the card in my hand, unable to speak.

"More than anything," Mason said, "this is what the tribe is for. Your father knew that without a structured way to use these effects for good—especially the Connection Effect—people had a tendency to slip. To drift slowly away. To lose the bonds that unite us."

Mason nodded at the letters he'd scratched in the rock.

"This tribe is a formula, Ethan," he said, "for creating the oldest, most powerful magic the world has ever known. And your father?" He looked down at the box in my hands. "Your father was the wizard."

Until now, my entire experience on the island had done nothing but reinforce how little I knew about my father.

Now, for the first time, I felt something shift. I felt some sense of *knowing*. A feeling of knowing my father not as the man who'd left us, and who cared for no one but himself, but as someone who cared about the people around him more than *anything*.

"I should have let him connect," I said, fighting back tears.

"We're all here to learn lessons," Mason said. "We don't always get to choose the timing. But that doesn't take make them mean any less."

We sat like that, in silence, me gripping the box, watching the sun finally clear the ocean and begin to rise into the sky.

"So now what?" I asked.

Mason placed a hand on the box in my lap.

"Your father wanted this to be his final resting place," he said.

He ran his fingers over the letters on the box, for the briefest of moments. Just a whisper of callous on wood.

And then he stood and walked away.

* * *

I watched the sea for some time, thinking about what Mason had said. About the tide that pulls us apart.

After some time, I pocketed the card he'd given me, then opened the box, and lifted the cloth bundle from inside.

I placed it on the warm stone of the mountain, and carefully unfolded its many layers. Inside, a mound of white ash lay stark against the black cloth.

I imagined my father sitting here for the first time. I wondered what he'd felt.

I realized that I'd never know. He was gone. But he'd left behind not just the most important lessons of his life, but a group of people to help me follow them. And, I realized, they *all* knew my father. Through them, I could not only follow my father's lessons, but learn to understand his life.

A slight breeze rose, building on the heat of the warming mountain. I watched a bird of prey rise in lazy, thermal circles, then drift away.

Ahead of me was the rising sun. Behind, the last of the night.

The breeze began to swell, rising up the sides of the mountain. A small puff of ash lifted from the cloth, and floated, dreamlike, off the summit and into the air where it seemed to vanish.

The breeze grew, and more ash lifted, carried away on the currents of wind and time. As I watched, a gust caught the last of the ash, carrying it away from me, northward. Toward Jasmine, and home. Toward my future.

I carefully closed the lid of the box.

I took one last look at the spreading rays of the sun, then I tucked the box under my arm and headed back in the direction of my tribe.

As I picked my way back down the footpath, I realized I'd never felt more connected to my father. It was as if some weight, some nagging doubt, carried for years, had finally been lifted.

And I realized something else.

It was time to go home.

CHAPTER 13
THE GIFT

The trip down the mountain was difficult, but not impossible. Walking downhill was harder than I thought, but I was fueled by a new purpose: *home*. Business was calling, yes. But more important, so were the other people in my life.

Since the moment I'd left the summit, I'd been consumed with the idea of heading home—home to Jasmine, home to our family and friends. The message of the Connection Effect had struck me deeply; I wanted to be with the most important people in my life.

Still, I knew that list of important people had grown this week. The intensity and novelty of the experiences I'd shared with the tribe had bonded me to them deeply; I was taking something with me, but I couldn't help feeling I was leaving something behind.

I walked near the back of the group, and from my higher vantage point on the downhill trail, I could see the entire tribe strung out before me, a long line of brothers winding their way down the mountain. In the middle of the pack, I spied the elders. There was the lanky Simon, with his fedora. Next, Vikram, with his white bristled hair standing stark against his brown skin. He seemed elf-like next to the towering figure of Terry, who loomed behind him, casting a shadow big enough to keep Vikram in near-constant shade.

Behind Terry, I caught the hyperactive bounce of Davis, the tiny man's laugh bubbling through the air as he tried in vain to trip Terry. And behind them, Bruce, the Aussie with his safari outfit and desert boots. And finally, the lean, rugged form of Mason the 'cowboy monk' who moved with a graceful, effortless stride.

As I watched them, I thought of the lessons each had taught me about the power of the right people to transform us.

Then the path entered the jungle, and the line of men disappeared from view.

* * *

The night torches were blazing, and they lit the path as I walked from my hut to the main lodge.

I was exhausted from the trip down the mountain, but I knew I would be gone before breakfast in the morning, and I wanted one last evening with my companions.

Plus, if my courage held—and I thought it would this time—there was one more thing I needed to do before my time here ended.

I arrived to find the main room lit with colorful patio lights. Tropical music played. There was a hum of cheerful conversation. For the first time since I arrived at the island, Mason had joined the crowd at the bar. The mood was clearly festive.

Mason smiled and waved me over, and I pulled up a stool next to him. From somewhere behind me, I heard the gleeful laughter of Davis, followed by some stern admonishment from Terry that I couldn't make out. Then a louder roar of laughter from the group.

It was warm and wonderful, and I felt a pang of sadness at the thought of leaving it behind.

Noticing my expression, Mason pointed his beer at a plaque that hung behind the bar:

The most important thing in life is to live for something more than just your own life.

– William James

"If I had a nickel for every time your father said that, I'd be a wealthy man."

I smiled. "I'm guessing you're already a wealthy man."

Mason shrugged. "My favorite part of being with the tribe is that I'm reminded that money is the least of our riches."

"I was thinking on the climb down," I said. "Why is it so hard to prioritize all these lessons? They seem so obvious right here and now. But I worry that back home I'll forget just how important all of this is."

Mason nodded in understanding. "That's the tide your father spoke of. The one that threatens to pull us apart."

"So how do we keep that from happening."

"You do what we all do," he said. "You never stop swimming."

He tapped the neck of his beer bottle against mine and took a long sip.

"Your father believed that a good life consists of one question," he said. "It's the most important one we can ever ask ourselves."

"What is it?"

Mason stared ahead. "We have a tendency to ask ourselves, *what's missing in my life?*" he said. "And the answer often leads us to things like wealth, or status, or possessions.

"In reality," he took another sip, "we should be asking not *what* is missing, but *who*." He turned to look at me. "That one question can change everything."

I nodded, and took a long swallow of my own beer. "I think my father picked a good person to take over as leader," I said.

Mason shook his head. "No. Roberto was adamant that he was just one part of something larger. He wasn't our leader. He was a catalyst to help us lead ourselves—individually, and as a group. That's the whole *point*. As long as we remind each other why we're *really* here—to forge bonds that enable us to *serve*—then we guide the tribe collectively. As long as we remember the effects, we're guiding ourselves, our tribe, our families and the world, to something better."

"So the tribe has no real leader?"

"Effectively, no. There are some of us who play parts, like your father. What truly leads us are the same effects you discovered this week. What leads us is the power of coming together."

I looked around the room, savoring the mood, the expressions of joy on the gathered faces. An arm touched here. Two heads bent in deep conversation there. And everywhere, laughter.

"Shouldn't be too tough a crowd for you," Mason said.

I felt my stomach tighten. I'd almost forgotten what I had ahead of me.

"I don't know," I said. "I just find it so hard to get up there and talk about myself. About my life."

Mason signaled to the bartender for another round, then turned on his stool to look at me.

"Let me reframe this for you," he said. "Every time you share. Every time you speak the truth. Every time you deliver your one-sheet, you're doing more than talking about yourself. You're doing more than asking for help. You're giving a gift to someone else."

"I don't understand," I said.

"When you share, authentically," he said, "you're reminding people that we *all* have goals. We all dream. But we all struggle, too. We all hurt. We all need *help.*"

The bartender placed two more beers in front of us.

"In that simple act of sharing," Mason said, "you do the most important thing of all. You remind us that we are all, in the end, human."

He raised his beer to me.

"The one-sheet isn't about you, Ethan," he said. "Not really. It's about *us.* All of us."

Before I could process his words, I heard the clinking of a glass, and the clamor in the room subsided. I turned on my barstool to find Simon standing, drink in hand.

"Before we get to dinner," he said, "I believe there's one more person who'd like to do their one-sheet."

Every head in the room swiveled to look at me. I took a last nervous sip of my beer, and then stood.

* * *

I started strong.

It still felt strange to tell the group the personal details of my health and my finances. But something had shifted. I knew these men, now. I *trusted* them. And so I pushed on.

But when it came time to talk about my relationships, I began to stumble.

"Let's see. For relationships. Uh. I know—I know that you all knew my fa—" I broke off.

I understood all I had to do was read what I had written on the page. To tell, in plain and simple terms, how my relationships were, and what I hoped for the future. And what was standing in my way.

But I was frozen in place.

How *could* I tell them? How could I explain that I had no *idea* how to create good relationships? That I would always wonder if I would be a good father. A good leader. A good *man*. That I was still chasing the ghost of a man I would never know—one who would never know *me*?

How could I tell them all that?

I looked toward the back of the room. Mason stood at the steps to the beach, leaning easily against the wooden framework, watching me closely.

He gave a single, slow, nod.

I heard his words echo back to me:

In that simple act of sharing you do the most important thing of all. You remind us that we are all, in the end, human.

I took a deep breath.

"I never knew my father," I began.

And the words flowed.

And when I finished and looked to the back of the room, Mason was gone.

* * *

The buzz of delivering my one-sheet was starting to fade as I made my way along the torch-lit path to my room. I knew its impact would continue long after the night was over, but now I felt a deep fatigue settling into my body. It had been a long couple of days.

I was about to climb into bed when I heard a knock at the door.

I opened it to find Simon on the porch, his face illuminated by torchlight. In his hands, he held a small cardboard box.

I stepped back to let him into the room.

"A week ago," he said, "you stood in my office and asked me, 'What do I get?' "

I flushed. "I'm sorry. That was rude."

Simon smiled warmly. "Not to worry. You were hurting, Ethan. Your father had died, a stranger to you. I hope that you've found some peace here. That some of that hurt is behind you."

It was, I knew. I felt it that night. My view of the world had changed this week, and along with it my view of my father. I'd found a peace I hadn't expected.

"I only wish…" I trailed off. What *did* I wish?

I'd learned so much about my father this week. I felt like I understood him. I'd even discovered, to my surprise, that I felt *proud* of him—of what he'd built. Of his legacy.

Yet, there was still that nagging sense that while I now knew him, he would never get a chance to know *me*. His final gift—the Connection Effect—would be something he'd never truly experience at the deepest level.

I realized that Simon was still waiting, patiently.

"Sorry," I said. "I was just thinking that I know so much about my father. It's a shame he never got to know me. I like to think—well, perhaps he might have been proud."

Simon gave me a strange look.

"What?"

He seemed to gather himself, and he regained his formal manner.

"Ethan," he said quietly. "I'm here to answer your question from last week." He paused as if wondering where to begin. "I know that you're expecting some—" he broke off. "Some financial consideration."

I flushed again. In truth, I had been. But that was a week—and a lifetime—ago.

"Maybe, in the beginning," I said. "But that... that was..." I searched for the right words, "a different... *me*."

Simon nodded. "Very well. You should know that your father left his financial estate to our tribal charity. He believed strongly that money was a force for good. It was a means to an end, not an end in itself. And as you know from hearing our one-sheets, we all give a large portion of our wealth to worthy causes."

I nodded. I didn't know what to say. The money did seem unimportant in light of everything I'd learned. But I couldn't deny that money might have helped solve my problems at home.

"The answer to your question of 'What do I get?' is *this*." Simon held out the box. "This is from your father. For you."

I took the box from Simon. It was a simple shoebox—old, battered around the edges, worn from much handling. It was from some long-defunct brand that I'd never heard of. On the lid was written in simple handwriting, *Ethan*.

I looked up at Simon. He nodded. "Open it," he said.

I lifted the lid.

The box was filled with photographs. All shapes and sizes. Some black and white. Some in color.

I picked up the top one. It was a photo of me as a baby. Beneath it was another: me again, this time grinning from the seat of a shiny two-wheeled bicycle. *I remember this*, I thought.

I dug deeper. There was me, graduating from high school. Another of me standing awkwardly with my prom date.

I looked up. "How did he get these? He left long before this."

Simon smiled knowingly. "A tribe is a wonderful thing, Ethan."

I felt my throat tighten. Tears pricked my eyes.

I looked through the box. There were photos from every important moment of my life. Our wedding—Jasmine, looking radiant, me looking shell-shocked but happy. There were Jasmine and I, arms around each other in front of a real estate 'for sale' sign.

Another, with the two of us holding paintbrushes, grinning like fools.

Me holding the first check from our business investors.

Us, at the Eiffel Tower.

"Turn them over," Simon said gently.

I flipped over one of my baby pictures. There was a sentence, handwritten in faded ink:

Your destiny is shaped by those around you.

I looked up at Simon in surprise.

"Your father was always connected to you. You were what motivated him. I would often find him, late at night, making his notes, your pictures spread out on his desk."

Simon nodded again at the photos. I turned over another—this one of me, at age five or so. A toothy, awkward grin. In the same handwriting was another faded phrase:

The right people reveal your richest source of power.

I began to pick up photos, turn them over. The back of each was marked up with notes, arrows, small diagrams. Bullet points. Some were crossed out. Reworded. But in all of them, I saw the seeds of what I had learned this week. Every effect.

They were all there, handwritten across a record of my life.

I realized I'd been holding my breath.

"How… how long," I whispered.

"Years. Many, many years," Simon said. "This was your father's gift to us. To the world. To *you*."

THE SIXTH EFFECT

SUMMARY

THE CONNECTION EFFECT

Your life will be measured
by the quality of your relationships

- A life dedicated to connection is a life free from regret.
- You are here to live in service to others.
- Connection is the greatest purpose of all.

CHAPTER 14
HOME

The knock came early.

The earliest glow of morning had yet to appear on the horizon, but the jungle was coming alive. The first cries of tropical life echoed through the morning silence. Dawn wasn't far off.

I opened the door. Once more, Simon stood on the porch.

"Ready?" he asked.

I nodded and took a last look around my hut. Considering how little time I'd spent in it, it felt remarkably like home.

Still, I knew home was elsewhere. Home was with Jasmine. Home was my work, my family, my friends.

We passed through the empty main lodge on our way to the waiting jeep. I scanned the bar area, hoping I might get one last farewell with the others, but the compound was dark and silent.

I felt a pang of sadness. In just a few short days, I'd gone from being a stranger in a foreign land to feeling a true sense of belonging. Now it felt as if things were running in reverse. Today, I'd leave everyone behind, even Simon.

We drove in silence through the pre-dawn. The headlights of the jeep lit the jungle walls to either side of the road. I pulled my jacket tighter in the damp chill.

"I feel like I'm leaving a part of me behind," I said at last.

Simon nodded thoughtfully, his eyes on the road. "Perhaps," he said, after a moment, "you are also taking something with you."

I settled back into the seat. He was right. I was taking an enormous amount with me. So why did I feel such a sense of loss?

* * *

The jeep pulled to a stop beside the small hut at the edge of the runway. It was still dark, but I thought I could see the barest glow on the horizon.

I pulled my bag from the back of the jeep and turned to face Simon.

"Is the plane here?"

"It's there."

I squinted in the darkness.

"Here," Simon said. He pulled a lighter from his pocket and lit a tall bamboo torch beside the hut. Its flickering glow did little to dispel the darkness, and I peered again in vain, trying to see the plane.

As I stared into the dark, another flame sputtered to life some twenty feet ahead of me. Seconds later, another flame appeared just a few feet past it. Then another.

As I watched, more and more torches flared to life, lighting the darkness and stretching in a long line across the open runway to a waiting jet.

There, in the growing glow of torchlight, I saw the tribe.

* * *

They were all there. Every one. Every elder, every member, had turned out to say goodbye. They stood, smiling, each holding a tall bamboo torch, forming a long line that stretched from where I stood.

I looked at Simon. He simply smiled and stepped aside, and I began to walk.

My vision began to blur with tears before I reached the first torch.

* * *

By the time I'd reached the last torch, my face was wet with tears, but I was smiling so much it hurt.

Each man had given me a firm handshake or a warm embrace. Each had offered short, powerful words of friendship and encouragement.

The last man in line was Mason. He looked as timeless as ever, stoic and strong. He shook my hand, then pulled me to him.

"Your father would be so proud of you," he whispered.

And then it was over.

* * *

I watched from the jet window as we lifted off. The torches of the tribe winked out one by one in the breaking dawn, and the island shrank, growing ever smaller until all I could make out was the volcanic peak where I had spread my father's ashes. Then we entered a bank of clouds, and I saw nothing. The island was gone.

As I turned away from the window and settled into my seat, it occurred to me that I still had no idea where the island even *was*. I thought back a week earlier to my struggles to explain to my team where I was going. At the time, I didn't know what to say. Here it was a week later and—the thought brought a genuine smile to my face—I *still* had no idea.

What *was* I going to say? The closer I got to home, the more the world of the island and the energy of the tribe began to be replaced by the reality of what I was returning to.

In an effort to stem my growing anxiety, I turned to my one-sheet. I reviewed my top five business goals. I looked at my aspirations for my health and my relationships. I knew I had to trust the process, and trust what I learned from the tribe, but I felt so uncertain.

I looked down at the shoebox on the seat beside me. My mind swirled with conflicting thoughts and emotions. I hadn't really expected my father to leave me a small fortune that would solve my problems, had I?

The truth was, the idea of a possible inheritance had been on my mind from the first moments in Simon's office. That was, after all, the reason I'd even shown up in the first place. It had been a lurking, almost distasteful truth that neither Jasmine nor I had spoken aloud. But it was there, nonetheless.

And although the idea of a financial estate had faded during my time with the tribe, I realized that it had never really left me. When I had told the team that I was retreating to solve the problems of the business, what I had really meant was that I was hoping to find a pot of gold at the end of a tropical rainbow.

I picked up the box and sat it on my lap. I'd found something more valuable than gold, I knew, and I wouldn't trade it for anything. But a shoebox of photographs and ideas wasn't something I could use to make payroll—I was right back where I started. My trip to the island was nothing more than just another last-ditch effort.

I looked at my watch. It was Friday. *How perfect*, I thought. *Another Hail Mary Friday.*

And another failure.

Now what the hell was I going to do?

* * *

Of course, the insight came from Jasmine.

I had been home for a week when she commented on how much more energetic I seemed. "And you're losing weight," she teased. "You should go away more often."

It was true, I realized. I'd been to the gym daily since I got home, and my eating habits had shifted. Something had happened to me during my time with the tribe. I could feel it.

Part of it was my one-sheet. The simple act of capturing my goals and tracking my progress was remarkable effective. But what had really made the difference was the local Tribe of Millionaires group that I'd joined. I hadn't met them in person yet, but already they were supporting me with daily encouragement. It was remarkable how the combination of accountability and friendship seemed to make all the difference. I was getting more done than ever, and still finding time to exercise and spend time with friends and family.

But still, the business was in a precarious position. I couldn't quite seem to right the ship. It just wasn't *flowing*.

It was Jasmine who helped me crack the code.

After seeing my transformation (and putting up with me talking endlessly about it for a week), she said off-handedly, "The effects are so powerful. It's too bad everyone can't experience them."

I'd agreed, of course, then continued blathering on about my amazing experience.

Later, though, her words came back to me—*it's too bad everyone can't experience them*—and I began to think about our business. Our job was to help gym and wellness centers improve retention by helping their members participate more. What I needed was to help our users—the customers who we were trying to motivate—to feel better about themselves. To do more, and as a result, *become* more.

What I realized, hearing Jasmine's words, was that I needed them to experience what *I* had.

I went upstairs to the bedroom and opened the bedside table. There, bundled with an elastic band, were the cards I'd received during my time on the island. I spread them out on the bed. Six cards. Six effects. Six lessons.

Was it possible?

I stood back and looked at the cards. Every effect was about the power of the right group of people to help us create better lives, and in turn, a better world.

Wasn't that what I was trying to do in my company? And if so, couldn't these six lessons help?

I considered my business. We'd been trying to help people, but every single step of the way, with every feature, every bit of code, every partner—we'd been thinking only of *individuals*. We'd never once considered the power of groups.

In hindsight, it was so obvious I felt like an idiot. Why hadn't I thought of the power of *connecting* these people to each other? After all, they were all trying to accomplish something challenging, trying to improve their lives—why not try *together*?

I felt my heart race. I knew—I *knew*—I was onto something. I bundled up the cards, hopped down the stairs two at a time, and flew through the kitchen, stopping just long enough to kiss Jasmine on the cheek.

"Gotta go to the office," I said.

"Now?"

"Now." I grabbed my coat. "Thank you!" I said.

"For what?"

"For everything," I called back.

Then I was out the door, my body in the car, my head in the clouds of a mysterious tropical island.

* * *

And so it was that, in the end, it wasn't money that solved my problem—it was the tribe.

More accurately, perhaps, it was my father.

Now that I look back, it seems so blindingly obvious: people didn't need rewards to make changes in their life. They didn't need money. What they needed was *other people*.

It wasn't easy. We did almost go bankrupt. Almost—it was close. The changes to the business took a little time, and time is money, as they say.

But time is also *life*. It's that thing you don't get more of. For the first time I felt like I was investing my time—my life—in something that truly mattered. I had, I realized, found a powerful *why*.

Within a month we had a new business model and a new approach—one that connected people as a way to help them make change. In effect, it created a tribe—a place for them to belong.

Along the way, it taught them all the effects I'd learned from my time on the island—and from my father. And the results were astonishing. Our beta users more than tripled their time at the gym. They got results. Our fitness and wellness business clients got what they wanted.

But that wasn't the best part.

Somewhere, somehow, the whole thing developed a life of its own. For months, we had pushed uphill, spending a fortune on advertising, attracting new users. Then… it just *went*, building up a wave of momentum. People started finding success, but then they started using the tools for things we'd never intended. They began to eat better. Make changes in their work, in their relationships. They began to connect more deeply with loved ones. They began to give back. They began to *connect*, in every best way possible.

Our efforts to create a business had started a movement. A *tribe*, one focused on positive change, connection, and abundance. One that taught that we truly are better together.

And so, in the end, you could say my Hail Mary worked. Not in the way I expected—there was no quick fix, no financial miracle.

But as I discovered, the right group of people is its own special kind of miracle.

You just need to find them.

THE END

LESSONS
TRIBE OF MILLIONAIRES

THE INFLUENCE EFFECT

Your destiny is shaped by those around you.

THE MULTIPLIER EFFECT

The right group of people compounds your efforts.

THE ACCOUNTABILITY EFFECT

Accountability is the world's most powerful force.

THE AUTHENTICITY EFFECT

You find your true self among those you trust.

THE PURPOSE EFFECT

The right people reveal your richest source of power.

THE CONNECTION EFFECT

*Your life will be measured
by the quality of your relationships.*

GOBUNDANCE
THE "REAL" TRIBE OF MILLIONAIRES

Tribe of Millionaires may be a fictional story, but there's more truth in these pages than you might realize.

This book is based on GoBundance, a real-life tribe created for the same reason that Ethan's father created Tribe of Millionaires: to help people become the best version of themselves.

It works. The effects in this book are all based on things that have happened time and time again to GoBundance members. We've watched firsthand as our tribe members use the power of surrounding themselves with the right people as a springboard to taking their lives to the next level and beyond.

Like so many good things, we created GoBundance because we needed it ourselves. We knew from painful experience how limiting and lonely life can be, even when you're on your way to success. GoBundance was our way of creating a reliable, productive way to lift each other up, and turn life into a fantastic adventure at the same time. It was our way of asking not *what* is missing from your life, as Ethan's father so eloquently phrased it, but *who*.

The result? We became healthier, happier, wealthier and felt like our lives—perhaps for the first time—were full of the most important things: close relationships, meaning, and a sense of purpose.

Like Ethan, many of our members were facing Hail-Mary moments of their own when they found GoBundance. We wanted to share with you some of their stories so you can see what happens when you make conscious decisions about the world around you. You'll find those stories in the pages that follow.

As our Ethan says, finding the right group of people is its own kind of miracle. We hope you'll agree.

To your epic life,

- The Founders of GoBundance

PS The "one-sheet" that Ethan discovers in the story is a real thing! You can download your own copy and get full video instruction on how to use it, all for free. We've also included our tribal tools for calculating your net worth and horizontal income. You'll find all that, and more, at:

www.TribeOfMillionaires.com

PROFILE
DIEGO CORZO

*"They gave me the confidence. Everything they told me
would take my life to the next level, I did.
They gave me the courage, they set a game plan for me,
and now here I am."*

— Diego

DIEGO CORZO was born in Lima, Peru and moved to the United
States with his family at the age of nine. His parents always told him
that America was the land of opportunity and that with persistence
and hard work he could accomplish anything.

Reality, it seemed, didn't quite agree.

As an undocumented immigrant, Diego found many doors closed
to him. Despite graduating third in his high school class and being
accepted into college, he realized that he wasn't eligible for student
loans or financial aid. Many of the scholarships that he won were

withdrawn because of his undocumented status. And to make things worse, his situation meant he couldn't find work to support himself as a student.

"But I was able to still find a way," Diego recalled. And he did, eventually graduating in the top 1% of his class and becoming a software developer.

Still, Diego had bigger dreams. He earned his real estate license and began educating himself by listening to podcasts from other realtors—including GoBundance elder Pat Hiban—hoping to learn how to improve.

"My dad told me that this is the land of opportunity," Diego said, "but it is up to us to find it. So no matter what obstacle I faced, I knew that there was a solution."

For Diego, that solution was GoBundance. With little more than the information on the website, he took a chance and attended a week-long group event in Steamboat, Colorado. It would be a pivotal choice.

As Diego recalled, "I needed to surround myself with individuals playing life at a big level. They challenged me. I turned 24 at the end of that event and I knew my life would never be the same."

Diego was right. Within four years, his net worth increased from $25,000 to over $600,000, and he now owns multiple real estate properties.

For Diego, however, the impact of GoBundance went far beyond wealth. "I used to stutter," he said, "I was always the kid in high school that would skip class so that I didn't have to read, write or talk or give a speech. I was afraid of talking on the phone.

"GoBundance lightened something in me. Now, I've told my story in front of 200, 300 people. I even gave a TEDx talk. It's something that I never, never imagined in my life, but those guys gave me the confidence."

PROFILE
AARON AMUCHASTEGUI

*"When you are surrounded by guys
that do amazing things,
they don't seem so impossible anymore."*

— AARON

AARON AMUCHASTEGUI found GoBundance at what, for him, was the ideal time. "I was needing a new fresh start and fire in my life," Aaron said. "My dad had just passed away, and when he died, I made a promise to myself and my family that from then on I would really go for it in life, and live every day like it is my last."

That, however, was easier said than done.

"Before GoBundance I was afraid of flying," Aaron recalled. "I wasn't athletic. I wasn't an adventure guy. I was kind of scared of life."

That's all changed. Since joining, he's done Ironman triathlons and been diving with great white sharks. He got his first passport in order to attend a GoBundance event. Now he's traveled the world with his family and flies 100,000 miles a year.

At his first event, Aaron noted that they asked everyone who had written a book to raise their hands. He was surprised and inspired by the count.

"I never thought I would write a book," he said, "but my wife and I wrote a book about the changes that occurred in our lives after joining GoBundance. It's a bestseller and is helping to change families."

The tribe also helped Aaron's business. Six months before joining GoBundance, he was broke. "Since then," Aaron said, "I've pretty much doubled my income, too."

Best of all, Aaron no longer feels isolated in his work. "I was really excited about business, but I was completely alone. I had nobody to talk to about the wins or the losses. And I remember feeling very free at that first event to be able to finally, for the first time, say those things."

PROFILE
JOHN EDWIN

*"We aren't one of these groups where
we're passing out business cards to each other.
We're not a networking group.
We are here to support one another
to be the best versions of ourselves."*

— John

JOHN EDWIN had spent nearly two decades becoming one of the premier personal trainers in the country. But for all his success, he was feeling unmoored.

"I had gone for a long time feeling, feeling like I was on an island," he said. "Like I was alienated, and I didn't have anyone to help me or someone to aspire to be like."

That all changed at his first GoBundance meeting. "As soon as I walked in," John said, "I knew I'd found my people. I knew it was the right place for me to be. I knew I was at home."

The timing was fortuitous. John had recently been forced from his training facility, and his business was in flux. With his life and business in transition, he joined GoBundance.

Within a year, he'd more than doubled his passive income, something he attributes entirely to his relationships within GoBundance.

"When I started getting involved and connecting with the caliber of the men there, I realize they're all setting the world on fire. It gave me something to aspire to, and people I could ask questions, to help understand things."

But the effects go deeper. Since getting his family involved, John's seen his three kids blossom. His oldest son, who struggled for years with a difficult health challenge, is now 15 and has even started his own online business.

"Every aspect of my life and my family's life has been impacted through GoBundance," John said. "I cannot put into words my gratitude towards this tribe."

PROFILE
DANIEL DEL REAL

I was grading my life at a different level.
What I thought was normal—it wasn't."

— Daniel

DANIEL DEL REAL was in his thirties when he was approached by GoBundance Elder Tim Rhode. "I was working a hundred hours a week," Daniel recalled, "and I was doing great. But I was working hard. I was neglecting my family a lot."

Tim convinced Daniel that there was more to a full life than wealth, and before long, Daniel found himself at a GoBundance event in Lake Tahoe where he faced his work habits head-on.

"They were asking me the important questions," he said. "What does that mean for your family? How's your health? How's your relationship with your kids?"

The more Daniel looked at his overworked life, the worse things seemed.

"I had pre-hypertension," he said. "I was pre-diabetic. I weighed 270 pounds. I was just not fit at all. I was overworked, overloaded, and suffering from panic attacks because I felt like there was just too much to do and not enough time."

With support from the tribe, Daniel reframed his approach to work and life. "I started getting myself into shape and I ended up doing a 70.3 Ironman in Austin," Daniel said. "That completely transformed my health. I've gone from not being able to run a mile to doing eight Ironman races."

Through it all, Daniel was also dealing with his long work hours. "I was addicted to my business," he recalled. "I was too scared to step away. They challenged me to have breakfast with my kids two days a week. They would text me in the morning to see if I was doing it."

It was hard at first, but the group supported Daniel, challenging him to make it work. And he did. Now, three years later, he's working a fraction of what he used to, spending time with his family every day, and his business is more efficient than ever.

PROFILE
WALLY ELIBIARY

*"It's very rare that you're able to find
a group of men that you can be
authentically transparent with
and you don't feel judged.
I've never had that my adult life
until GoBundance."*

— Wally

WALLY ELIBIARY was 14 when his family turned their back on him. As a teenager trying to grow up on his own, he struggled with challenges of trust and self-worth. As an adult, it was his peers in GoBundance who offered him a place to be himself.

"They allowed me to be me instead of trying to be who I thought they wanted me to be," Wally said.

Surrounding himself with successful people he trusted and who hold him accountable has allowed Wally to change his approach to work and life.

"I was the one that always worked really hard—no one outworked me. Through GoBundance I was able to learn how to work smart and have others work hard for me. I was able to learn from them how to turn three steps into two steps."

That education has paid off. Since joining, Wally's been able to double his income. He no longer works evenings or weekends, and he's taken twenty weeks of vacation in the last year—more than ten times what he ever had before.

Much of that freedom has come from developing passive income. "When I joined GoBundance," Wally said, "I owned zero rental properties. Today I own 59."

But the single biggest motivator for Wally isn't wealth or accomplishment, or the 25 pounds he's lost. It's his family.

"There are people in your family that deserve a better version of you," Wally said. "It could be a more loving person. It could be a better listener. It could be a better role model or a better man of faith. It can be a healthier husband that can be there for your family."

PROFILE
JOHN WHITE

"You have a group of people
who wouldn't be where they are
if they weren't confident,
and yet they have this sense of humility.
It's unique."

— John

JOHN WHITE is a wealth manager. He's accustomed to being around successful people. But as his thirtieth birthday approached and he was beginning to find his own business success, he realized there were limits to what he could share with others.

It was GoBundance Elder David Osborn who told him, "Sometimes you get to a place where you have your biggest win in life and you can't really tell anybody else."

John remembers thinking, "I need that—other guys who are doing things similar or bigger, who you can celebrate your biggest wins with and no one is going to judge you."

It turned out that his new peers would offer much more. At one event, John recalled a poignant moment during a GoBundance adventure.

"We're having a very vulnerable conversation about our personal relationships," he said. "And I remember looking over the mountains, thinking, *I didn't even know these guys three days ago.* I remember just how good it felt to have a conversation like that with people that I knew had no reason to judge me. And to do it at the top of a beautiful mountain where you can see for miles."

After more than half a decade with the group, John sees his GoBundance membership as a unique investment, even to his seasoned wealth manager's eyes.

"When you invest in a financial asset," he said, "you've usually got only a couple of ways that money is working for you. The return on GoBundance is holistic. You're getting a return in yourself; you're getting return in your relationships. You're getting a return on your business. Where else am I going to get that?"

ARE YOU READY TO PLAY AT A HIGHER LEVEL?

To learn more about GoBundance membership, please visit www.GoBundance.com

ABOUT THE AUTHORS

DAVID OSBORN

David Osborn is a *New York Times* bestselling author of the books *Wealth Can't Wait* and *Miracle Morning Millionaires*, and is co-owner of the sixth largest real estate company in the U.S., with an excess of $10 billion in sales. In addition to being a primary investor and operator of countless real estate-related businesses, he is Co-Founder & Chairman of Magnify Capital, a private equity firm in Austin. Overall, he has done business in more than forty U.S. states and in Canada.

Firmly rooted to the principle of knowledge-sharing and giving back, David is a founder and operating partner of GoBundance and is the leader of the Champions Division there. Further, David sits on the boards of the 1Life Fully Lived nonprofit and Habitat for Humanity Austin. He contributes to various causes including

Charity Water and the Dell Children's Hospital.

David is the proud father of two amazing daughters and one son and is married to the wonderful and talented Traci Osborn.

PAT HIBAN

Pat Hiban started out as a real estate agent fresh out of college and hustled his way to top honors at multiple companies, eventually becoming the #1 agent in the world at Re/Max International. Over time he invested in horizontal lines of income and retired from full-time real estate sales at 46 years of age. He is the author of the *New York Times* Bestseller *6 Steps to 7 Figures* and the co-founder of GoBundance. Pat actively plans the international bucket list trips for the GoBros and hosts the GoBundance Podcast as well as his own podcast – Real Estate Rockstars. His family includes 2 daughters, Heather and Kayli, and a wife of almost three decades, Kim. He resides in both Folly Beach, South Carolina and Columbia, Maryland.

MIKE MCCARTHY

Mike McCarthy is Co-owner and Operating Partner for the Greater Pennsylvania Region of Keller Williams Real Estate. He is a Co-Founder of GoBundance and is the leader behind FamBundance an organization that teaches families to connect more deeply and build their family legacy together. He has co-authored *The Miracle Morning for Parents and Families* along with his wife Lindsay and Bestselling Author Hal Elrod. His GoBros affectionately refer to Mike as "McLovin," and he resides in a suburb of Philadelphia PA with his wife and two children.

TIM RHODE

Tim Rhode comes from a very humble background, growing up in a blue-collar family in a rural blue-collar town. His family's tight financial situation left an indelible mark on Tim, and although he barely graduated high school and never attended college, Tim went on to dream, plan, and create his own "magnificent life" and retired financially free at the age of 40. Tim is one of the founders of Gobundance, and also the Founder/ CEO and visionary behind 1Life Fully Lived; a non-profit organization he started in 2011. He is totally committed to helping people of all ages plan their best future, including helping transform the "life education" of young people. Tim's passions include his family, skiing, hiking, and mountain biking. Tim has three grown children and lives in Portola, California with his wife Tina.

ACKNOWLEDGEMENTS

The Authors would like to first and foremost thank their families. The Osborns: Traci, Cheaven Roberts, Bella, Luke, and David's sister Ann E. Osborn. The Hibans: Kim, Heather, and Kayli. The McCarthys: Lindsay, Tyler, and Ember. The Rhodes: Tina, Chris, Sarah, and Andy. And of course, to all of our parents who helped make us the human beings we are today. Next, we'd like to thank Dan Clements who traveled all the way to Japan to meet with 22 GoBros on an international bucket list adventure so he could help us put our company's soul into an incredible story. Thank You to Rock Thomas, Joe Polish, Gary Keller and Front Row Dads. To Joshua Dorkin, David Greene,Brandon Turner, and the entire Bigger Pockets organization. To Robert Herjavec, Robert Kiyosaki, Sean Stephenson, Aubrey Marcus, Rob Dial, J.P. Sears, Charlie Engle, Ben Hardy, Jeff Hoffman, and all the other speakers we have been honored to have at our events, thanks for enriching our lives. We would also like to thank our original mentor who taught us the value of a mastermind and extreme accountability: Dr. Fred Grosse.

To Jon Berghoff, our newest Gobundance Elder- for designing, leading and transforming our annual mastermind events, for co-founding and bringing the Gobundance Women's tribe to life - you have enabled us to grow and evolve exponentially, since the day you arrived!!!

It's important for us to recognize our first official class of GoBundance. This group of founding members believed in our vision so much that they put up hard-earned money to join without it having proven itself yet.

Adam Roach, Andrew Cushman, Bob Wells, Brett Levine, Dan Grieb, Darren McMahon, Diego Corzo, Gabe Deukmaji, Gary Jonas, John White, Mark Jeffries, Mark Schwaiger, Matt Aitchison, Mo Choumil, Paul Morris, Samuel Wegert, Saul Zenkevicius, Wally Elibiary

Then we would like to thank our Champion Members, who inspire us all on a daily basis (Champions have a verified net worth of over 5 million dollars and/or earn an adjusted gross income of one million dollars annually):

Aaron Amuchastegui, Aleksandar Memca, Arnold Kozys, Dan Lesniak, Daniel Del Real, Daniel Ramsey, Dave Codrea, Gary Jonas, John White, Josh Friedensohn, Kamil Maras, Michael Hananel, Nate Martinez, Nick Waldner, Paul Morris, Rick Hale, Scott Smith, Steven Hatcher, Vitalijus Kaleinikovas, Wally Elibiary

Our badassadors past and present who have stepped up as leaders and gatekeepers for our organization, showing that we are truly a member-led tribe:

Adam Roach, Cory Older, Diego Corzo, Erle Thompson, Fred Hubler, Josh Painter, Matt Aitchison, Matt Templeton, Mario Mazzamuto, Pat Cullinane, Shawn Lowery

Thank you to our Growth Partners who have been massively influential in helping us grow:

Aaron Amuchastegui, Adam Roach, Bob Wells, Brandon Turner, Cory Older, Dan Grieb, David Osborn, David Greene, Erle Thompson, Hal Elrod, Hans Box, John White, Josh Friedensohn, Mario Mazzamuto, Matt Aitchison, Matt Faircloth, Matt Donnelly, Mike McCarthy, Mo Choumil, Neal Collins, Patrick Hiban, Patrick Cullinane, Rock Thomas, Saul Zenkevicius, Shawn Lowery, Steven Hatcher, Tim Rhode

And to the entire tribe of high achieving men, who, without your energy and willingness to grow and embrace the beliefs of GoBundance, this book would have never been written!!

Aaron Amuchastegui, Aaron Velky, Aaron West, Adam Cole, Adam Roach, AJ Osborne, Alan Schnur, Aleksandar Memca, Andre Kajlich, Andrew Cushman, Andy Gilbert, Anthony Vigilante, Anton Bayer, Arnold Kozys, Bart Swinnen, Beau Eckstein, Ben Balsbaugh, Ben Riehle, Bob Wells, Brandon Rumbley, Brandon Turner, Brendan Lawrence, Brent Flewelling, Brett Levine, Brian Galura, Brian Murray, Brian Oatis, Brian Overly, Brian Wentz, Buddy Martin, Calvin Chin, Casey Wright, Cav Vassau, Chad Swanson, Charlie Engle, Chris Dufala, Chris Dunham, Chris Lochhead, Chris Marrone, Chris Papa, Chris Plough, Christopher Savino, Chuong Pham, Cody Bjugan, Cody Littlewood, Cooper Callaway, Cory Nemoto, Cory Older, Courtney Atkinson, Craig Jones, Dan Grieb, Dan Lesniak, Dan Trinidad, Dana Amato, Daniel Casey, Daniel Del Real, Daniel Nunney, Daniel Perez, Daniel Ramsey, Darren McMahon, Darsh

Singh, Dave Codrea, David Greene, David Lawver, David Mantek, David Osborn, David Sollis, Dean Devries, Denton Aguam, Derek Blain, Derek Weichel, Devin Elder, Diego Corzo, DJ Savoy, Don Hayley, Eddie Overdyke, Eric Forney, Erik M Hardy, Erle Thompson, Frank Smollon, Fred Hubler, Gabe Deukmaji, Gabriel Hamel, Garrett Gunderson, Gary A Jonas Jr, Gary Wilson, Gino Barbaro, Hal Elrod, Hans Box, Ian Kurth, Ian Meierdiercks, Ian Milligan-Pate, Imran Khan, Jace Mattinson, Jack Yen, Jake Harris, James Cowherd, Jamie Gruber, Jared Addis, Jason Baxter, Jason Griggs, Jason Parisella, Jason Shinpaugh, Jay Bourgana, Jeff Delone, Jeffrey Block, Jeremy Mathis, Jeremy Reisig, Jeremy Taylor, Jim Campbell, Jim Sheils, JJ Mueller, John Antonelli, John Edwin, John White, Jon Berghoff, Jon Wanberg, Jonathan Holt, Jordan Bennett, Joseph Colasuonno, Joseph Gozlan, Josh Friedensohn, Josh McCallen, Josh Mente, Josh Painter, Joshua Lewis, Justin Jarboe, Kamil Maras, Kelly Gilson, Ken Wimberly, Kendall Kirk, Kevin Swartz, Kurt Buchert, Kyle Fogg, Lon Breitenbach, Marcelo Munoz, Mario Mazzamuto, Mark Berns, Mark Jackson, Mark Jeffries, Mark Malevskis, Mark Schwaiger, Mark Walker, Martin Eiden, Matt Aitchison, Matt DeBoth, Matt Donnelly, Matt Faircloth, Matt Hermes, Matt Holm, Matt Lenza, Matt O'Neill, Matt Shaw, Matt Templeton, Max Paisley, Michael Tomasetti, Michael Hananel, Michael Pouliot, Miguel Cordova, Mike Aiello, Mike Ayala, Mike Dillard, Mike McCarthy, Mike Nuss, Mike Sroka, Mo Choumil, Moe Mathews, Muhizi Condo, Nate Martinez, Nathan Leinen, Nathaniel Smith, Neal Collins, Nicholas DeMaiolo, Nick Romano, Nick Santonastasso, Nick Waldner, Paresh Mehta, Pascal Wagner, Pasha Esfandiary, Patrick Cullinane, Pat Hiban, Paul Mead, Paul Morris, Paul

Sloate, Randy Visser, Ratmir Rafikov, Ray Bayat, Richard Biechler, Richard Sherman, Rick Bosl, Rick Hale, Robert Fitzgerald, Robert Creamer, Robert Shoemaker, Rock Thomas, Ryan Paquin, Ryan Pineda, Sam Monreal, Samuel Wegert, Saul Zenkevicius, Scott Haire, Scott Smith, Sean McGovern, Seth Dailey, Shane McCullar, Shawn Lowery, Stephen Castro, Steve Dye, Steven Hatcher, Tariel Gusseinov, Ted Brockman, Tim Rhode, Tom Donnelly, Tommy Christy, Tony Sarenpa, Tony Trinh, Travis Baucom, Vitalijus Kaleinikovas, Wally Elibiary, Will Yoder, Wyatt Graves

And to our founding members of GoBundance Women. We look forward to the incredible innovations you will create that will inspire women around the world.

Ariel Bertsch, Gayle Bertsch, Shanna Blanton, Karen Briscoe, Terese Brittingham, Bianca Bucuram, Megan Butler, Aileen Castellano, Adair Cates, Cathleen Christen, Linzee Ciprani, Gabrielle Clayman, Kelly Clements, Penelope Cuevas, Brianna Greenspan, Jaime Hope, Micaela Hornstein, Shannon Huffer, Felicia Keith-Jones, Amrita Khurana, Alexandra Kontos, Christine Lee, Nicole Lenz, Janel Loughin, Angie Macdougall, Michele McBride, Asmaa Methqal, Wendy Mueller, Lindsay Musser, Vanessa Peters, Dolores Quinonez, Kelly Resendez, Chelsea Rodriguez, Tanya Salseth, Saba Shoaeioskouei, Jamie Smith, Lindsay Smith, Marni Task, Sherry Thacker, Lorri Wolfe

To learn more about GoBundance Women membership, please visit www.GoBundanceWomen.com

Thank You to the GoWives who have stood next to their men on the rollercoaster that is entrepreneurship. Without their undying love, support and overall badassery in their own right, their men could not shine so brightly. A special Thanks to those who joined us in Arizona and Costa Rica to learn more about themselves and develop relationships with other women who truly understand each other.

Andrea Del Real, Amber Wimberly, Esther Parisella, Jen Choumil, Jenn West, Jill Friedensohn, Kaleena Amuchastegui, Kellie Overly, Kristina Baucom, Koreen Thompson, Laura Kaleinkovas, Lindsay McCarthy, Patricia Maras, Rosi Zenkevivius, Sarah Codrea, Shelby Campbell, Traci Osborn, Vilma Kozys, Whitney Ramsey

We would like to thank our Fambundance Member Families, for trusting us with your most precious asset and allowing us to all Grow together, knowing that our legacies is only as strong as the hands we equip to carry them forward. For more information on our Family events and programs, please visit www.fambundance.com

Amuchastegui Family, Dailey Family, DelReal Family, Edwin Family, Maras Family, Massey Family, McCarthy Family, Osborn Family, Overly Family, Sarenpa Family, West Family, Block Family, Casey Family, Choumil Family, Clidy Family, Elibiary Family, Gusseinov Family, Hatcher Family, Kirk Family, McBride Family, McCallen Family, Mueller Family, Thompson Family

Big hug and thanks to the incredible behind-the-scenes team at GoBundance... our GoTeam!!

Ally Evangelista, Braden Deloneay, Cecil Cummins, Dani Lipsky, Elizabeth Santiago, Jeff Tucker, Khary Alexcee, Matt Duncan, Melanie Andreetta, Minnie Torres, Missy Hacker, Sam Webster

And a big shout-out and thanks to our helpful book team as well:

Honorée Corder, Jackie Dana, Dino Marino

Special TY to Mr. Dirk van Reenen
and Jeremy "Brotha James" Reisig.

The Charity of Choice for GoBundance is 1Lifefullylived.
Go to http://1lifefullylived.org for more information

Made in the USA
Coppell, TX
19 June 2021